McDougal Littell Middle School
Math
COURSE 1

Larson   Boswell   Kanold   Stiff

Professional Development Book

The Professional Development Book contains a wide variety of professional development materials. Included are suggestions for in-service workshops, a section on using rubrics to grade open-response items and projects, and professional articles and activities on reading, vocabulary, problem solving and critical thinking. Math background notes, tips for new teachers, parental involvement pages, and ideas for bulletin boards are also provided.

McDougal Littell
A HOUGHTON MIFFLIN COMPANY

Evanston, Illinois • Boston • Dallas

Copyright © 2004 by McDougal Littell Inc.
All rights reserved.

Permission is hereby granted to teachers to reprint or photocopy in classroom quantities the pages or sheets in this work that carry a McDougal Littell copyright notice. These pages are designed to be reproduced by teachers for use in their classes with accompanying McDougal Littell material, provided each copy made shows the copyright notice. Such copies may not be sold and further distribution is expressly prohibited. Except as authorized above, prior written permission must be obtained from McDougal Littell Inc. to reproduce or transmit this work or portions thereof in any other form or by any other electronic or mechanical means, including any information storage or retrieval system, unless expressly permitted by federal copyright laws. Address inquiries to Manager, Rights and Permissions, McDougal Littell Inc., P.O. Box 1667, Evanston, IL 60204.

ISBN: 0-618-28028-6

56789-MDO-07 06 05 04

Contents

How to Use This Handbook	1
Alternative Assessment and Scoring Rubrics	3
Classroom Activities	13

Chapter Support Materials

Chapter 1	29
Chapter 2	36
Chapter 3	43
Chapter 4	50
Chapter 5	57
Chapter 6	64
Chapter 7	71
Chapter 8	78
Chapter 9	85
Chapter 10	92
Chapter 11	99
Chapter 12	106
Chapter 13	113
Answer Key	A1

Contents

In-Service Workshop Outlines These pages can help teachers plan and conduct in-service programs at their own schools. The material includes suggestions and planning guidelines for successful in-service programs.

Alternative Assessment and Scoring Rubrics This section provides guidance to teachers on how to use rubrics to grade open-response items on test and student projects. The section includes discussions about what a rubric is and how to apply a rubric to a test item or a project, as well as how to grade some practical examples of student work.

Classroom Activities These are activities for students to do in class. There are four types of activities: reading, vocabulary, problem solving, and critical thinking, each introduced with material to help teach the concepts. Reading activities focus on helping students to better read verbal problems. Vocabulary activities focus on helping students better understand the vocabulary in each chapter. Problem solving activities focus on helping students better understand various problem solving strategies. Critical thinking activities focus on helping students use critical thinking.

Math Behind the Math These notes provide background on the mathematics of the lesson, including mathematical ideas that teachers may wish to share with students. The notes provide help and support for both experienced and new teachers.

Tips for New Teachers These teaching notes provide both new and experienced teachers with useful teaching tips for each lesson, and include tips about common errors and inclusion.

Parents as Partners These pages help parents contribute to student success by providing an overview of the chapter, along with questions and activities for parents and students to work on together.

Ideas for Bulletin Boards These are suggestions for creating a bulletin board to reinforce key concepts in each chapter. Included are the materials needed, ideas for how to create the bulletin board, and suggestions for activities based on the bulletin board.

How to Use This Handbook

This handbook serves two purposes. Use it as a guide for leading middle school Math in-service workshops and as a resource for teaching middle school math.

Assessing Student Work

The first section of this handbook provides information on assessing student work. It includes background information on alternative assessment and holistic scoring. It also includes specific suggestions for creating scoring rubrics. The samples of student work provided can be photocopied and given to teachers to "practice score" during an in-service workshop.

Implementing the Curriculum

- To aid teachers in reaching all students, the *Classroom Activities* section provides specific teaching strategies for *problem solving*, *critical thinking*, *reading*, and *vocabulary*. Sample activities that can be photocopied and used in a workshop or the classroom are included.

- To give teachers support for each lesson, the *Math Behind the Math* section gives teachers a quick overview of each chapter's math topic and its importance within the entire math course. The *Tips for New Teachers* section provides ideas for implementing the lesson, suggestions for spotting common errors and activities to foster inclusion in the classroom.

- To help teachers communicate with families, a letter to parents, called *Parents as Partners*, is written for each chapter. This letter summarizes the math topic being studied and suggests how parents can help their student learn the topic.

Motivating Your Students

The *Bulletin Board Ideas* section provides creative ideas that are easy to display and that relate to key math topics within each chapter. One *Bulletin Board Idea* in each unit suggests ways in which the unit poster can be used as a bulletin board. One poster is provided for each unit of the program.

Presenting and Exploring Middle School Math

As an in-service guide, this handbook provides outlines for in-service workshops of varying lengths. Many of the overview materials are found in the Student Edition and the Teacher's Edition. More specific materials, such as strategies for teaching math vocabulary and ideas for bulletin boards, are also in this handbook.

In-service Workshop Outlines

One-half Day In-service

Workshop Overview	Handbook Pages	Other Materials
Introduction to the Program		Teacher's Edition, pages T21–T39
Organization of Student Book		Student Edition, pages vi–xix
Focus on One Section		Student Edition, pages 312–332, tiles (counters, pennies, colored squares of paper), graph paper
Assessing Student Work	Pages 3–12	
Teacher Support Materials	Pages 73–79	Teacher's Edition, page T28–T33

1-Day In-service

Workshop Overview	Handbook Pages	Other Materials
Introduction to the Program		Teacher's Edition, pages T21–T39
Organization of Student Book		Student Edition, pages vi–xix
Focus on One Section		Student Edition, pages 312–332
Hands-on Activities		Student Edition, pages 318–319, tiles (counters, pennies, or colored squares of paper), graph paper
Technology Activities		Student Edition, page 355, calculators
Problem Solving Lessons		Student Edition, pages 41–45, 325, Exercise 50
Teaching Strategies for *Problem Solving* and *Critical Thinking*	Pages 21–28	
Teaching Strategies for *Reading* and *Math Vocabulary*	Pages 13–20	
Assessing Student Work	Pages 3–12	Student Edition, pages 358–361
Teacher Support Materials	Pages 71–77	Teacher's Edition, pages T28–T33

2-Day In-service

Workshop Overview	Handbook Pages	Other Materials
Introduction to the Program		Teacher's Edition, pages T21–T39
Organization of Student Book		Student Edition, pages vi–xix
Focus on One Section		Student Edition, pages 312–332
Hands-on Activities		Student Edition, pages 318–319, tiles (counters, pennies, colored squares of paper), graph paper
Technology Activities		Student Edition, page 355, calculators
Problem Solving Lessons		Student Edition, page 41–45, 325, Exercise 50
Teaching Strategies for *Problem Solving* and *Critical Thinking*	Pages 21–28	
Teaching Strategies for *Reading* and *Math Vocabulary*	Pages 13–20	
Assessing Student Work	Pages 3–12	Student Edition, pages 358–361
Motivating Students	Page 77	Unit 2 poster
Communicating with Parents	Pages 75–76	
Teacher Support Materials	Pages 71–74	Special Activities Book Teacher's Edition, pages T28–T33

Alternative Assessment and Scoring Rubrics

Introduction

As a teacher, the most important information you can have about your students is what they already know and what they have yet to learn. Obtaining this information for you is the purpose of assessment. Assessment should be a process rather than a product; it should guide and enrich student learning of mathematics, and help inform and guide the instruction of mathematics. It is not just to obtain a grade for students and teachers. The Mathematical Science Education Board (MSEB) states that assessment in mathematics should accomplish the following goals:

- Promote the development of mathematical power for all students.
- Measure the full range of mathematical knowledge, skills, and processes specified by the standards set forth by the National Council of Teachers of Mathematics (NCTM).
- Communicate to students, parents, and teachers what mathematics students already know, as well as the mathematics they have yet to learn.

To accomplish these goals, assessment needs to go beyond multiple-choice and single-answer questions. It needs to include rich, complex problems, grounded in real-world or mathematical contexts, for students to solve, and it needs to allow students to communicate their solution strategies and processes.

Assessment should reflect the mathematics that all students need to know and be able to do, and it should focus on students' understandings as well as their procedural skills.

From NCTM's *Principals and Standards for School Mathematics*

Many students, however, dismiss and resist the need to communicate in the mathematics classroom. They think of mathematics in terms of getting a right answer and prefer to leave their communication skills at the door of their English classroom. Communicating strategies and process, however, is essential if teachers, students, and parents are to understand the full range of students' skills and understanding. The most effective way to overcome this resistance is to assess it.

Alternative Assessment

Because of the multiple learning styles in a classroom, students should have the opportunity to communicate their mathematical thinking in many ways. All the following modes of assessment can and should be included.

- Responses to open-ended questions, problems, and tasks
- Projects and investigations
- Mathematics portfolios
- Writing in mathematics
- Demonstrations, discussions, and presentations
- Observations, interviews, and conferences

These modes of assessment work together in a complimentary manner to provide several views of students' abilities and skills.

Assessment should support the learning of important mathematics and furnish useful information to both teachers and students.

Principles and Standards for School Mathematics, from the National Council of Teachers of Mathematics (NCTM)

Once students are regularly communicating their thinking processes using these types of alternative assessments, students, teachers, and parents reap many benefits. For teachers, the benefits include:

- Informing them of a student's proficiency and depth of understanding in specific content areas;
- Informing them of a student's proficiency and depth of understanding in specific content and process standards (both NCTM standards and state specific standards);
- Documenting to parents, administrators, and the community at large the progress made by students in all areas of mathematical study; and
- Guiding them toward making instructional decisions.

For students, assessment tasks can help them to grow not only mathematically but also as life-long learners by helping them set goals for themselves, assume responsibility for their own learning, and become independent problem solvers. For parents, assessment tasks demonstrate exactly what skills and concepts their children have mastered and what their children have yet to learn. These tasks increase parents' awareness of the process of problem solving, not just "getting the answer," and documents for them how a "grade" or score to a problem was obtained.

Holistic Scoring

Despite all the advantages of using alternative assessments, the difficulties of scoring these problems and tasks cannot be underestimated. Trying to maintain consistency from student to student and from problem to problem often results in one agonizing decision after another. Beyond the time spent reading and analyzing the solutions and solution processes, teachers spend much valuable time just trying to decide at what level the student is working. What is needed is a way to score student responses that are consistent and reliable.

Consistency and reliability can be achieved by establishing reference criteria for each problem or task. Holistic scoring, that is, scoring that reflects all aspects of the solution and the solution process, is an effective method for establishing a standard. Each of the following aspects of the solution should be considered when assessing the adequacy of a student response.

THE TASK Does the student show a clear understanding of the task? Does the student define the task in terms of the mathematical solution needed? Does the student approach the problem in a recognizable form?

THE CHOICE OF A STRATEGY Does the student select an appropriate strategy for finding a solution?

THE APPLICATION OF THE STRATEGY Does the student select relevant information as data for the solution process? Does the student complete all aspects of the solution process, such as creating a table or a graph? Does a guess-and-check strategy have a recognizable form? Is the answer given in terms of the problem, with appropriate units and accurate descriptors?

COMPUTATIONAL ACCURACY Does the work show no, or few, errors in arithmetic? If an error is made in the first step with no additional errors, the problem should be scored based on one error, not on errors at every step of the solution.

COMMUNICATION Does the student justify his or her answer in mathematical terms using grade-level appropriate grammatical conventions? Are all explanations clear and complete? Do all graphs and tables have labels that clarify the data?

By assigning points to these five aspects of a problem or task, a teacher can create a set of reference criteria for scoring, called a scoring rubric. The number of points assigned to a task should be relative to the sophistication of the problem and the difficulty of the solution steps. When teachers keep these aspects of holistic scoring in mind, creating item-specific rubrics and evaluating student work against these rubrics becomes standard practice. The use of rubrics eases the burden on the teacher by removing the time spent making and then rethinking decisions on each student's work.

Using Holistic Scoring to Create Rubrics

Scoring rubrics allow assessment to be informative and consistent from student to student and from problem to problem. In a scoring rubric, a small number of points are awarded (usually 3 to 5) for attempting or completing the holistic aspects of an open-ended task. For scoring rubrics to be effective, a rubric should be applied to the scoring of all open-ended tasks that are assigned.

Assessment should become a routine part of the ongoing classroom activity rather than an interruption.

From NCTM's *Principals and Standards for School Mathematics*

Depending upon the breadth of an open-response problem or task, a 3-, 4-, or 5-point rubric can be developed specifically for it. The presentation of the problem should include the number of points to be awarded for a complete solution. This alerts a student to the extent that he or she should respond to the question.

To customize a scoring rubric to the complexity of an open-response problem or task, points can be allocated to the aspects of holistic scoring in a manner that best fits the problem. Often the following distribution works well.

3-POINT HOLISTIC SCORE One point is awarded for each of the following.

- The answer is arithmetically correct.
- The answer is justified by some process.
- The process is communicated clearly by the student.

4-POINT HOLISTIC SCORE Points are awarded for each of the following.

- All computations are correct for the two or more steps in the solution process. (2 points)
- The answer is justified by some process. (1 point)
- The process is communicated clearly by the student. (1 point)

5-POINT HOLISTIC SCORE Points are awarded for each of the following.

- All computations are correct. (3 points)
- Multiple steps are identified as part of the solution process. (1 point)
- The process and answer are justified by the student. (1 point)

A more detailed chart of these criteria is shown on page 12.

Students should know that a rubric will be applied to all open-response problems and tasks. With experience, they should be able to anticipate the requirements of each rubric. To use rubrics effectively, students need to solve many open-ended problems and to repeatedly analyze the application of the rubric to their own solutions. Examples of exemplary work and adequate answers will help students become better problem solvers.

Pages 8–12 show the application of a scoring rubric to one sample problem taken from the student text. These pages include a statement of the problem, the rubric used, four samples of student work, and a sample complete solution. You may want to share with students the item-specific rubric and the complete solution on pages 8 and 11 at the beginning of the school year. These pages will show them how open-response items are scored and what a complete solution is. At other times during the year, you may want to share outstanding student work with the class, again to help them understand what is expected. When students see that many solutions and solution processes are possible, they will begin to feel more comfortable with open-response items and the importance of communicating their thinking.

Implementing Scoring Rubrics in the Classroom

Most students have not been assessed using scoring rubrics before and cannot anticipate the implications of their use. It is the responsibility of the teacher to prepare students to use them successfully. Several activities can help in this preparation.

First, students need many experiences in solving open-response problems and tasks in an informal setting before formal assessment is implemented. These informal experiences need to include feedback to the student on how closely their work matched expectations. Classroom discussions, written comments, and conferences with individual students all work well. For reluctant communicators, conferencing can be especially helpful. When students have difficulty expressing their processes and strategies, often they can still respond positively when asked "How did you get this answer?" They can then use their own comments as a writing prompt for writing a justification of their solution process.

A second activity is to have students grade work that other students have done. By evaluating how completely and correctly the anonymous solutions fit the problem or task, students begin to understand what a complete response includes. These anonymous works can be gleaned from students in other classes, in other grades, or from classes the teacher has taught in previous years.

A third way to help students respond positively to rubrics is to post reminder notices in the classroom about expectations, such as the one below.

SUCCESS Rules for Open-Response Problem Solving

Show your work on the same page as the question.

Use correct labels on all answers.

Check your work. Did you answer the question asked in the problem?

Correctly label scales and coordinates when graphing an answer. Include a title.

Explain your process clearly and concisely.

Specific examples used in an explanation must be mathematically correct.

Scorers are not mind readers; make sure your explanation is clear.

Only after multiple experiences with all three types of activities should teachers try to assess their students formally using holistic scoring rubrics. Only then will students have the background knowledge needed for success.

Conclusion

Once students understand the basis for the scoring system, they have a good idea of what is expected of them. They begin to understand that part of every open-response answer includes statements about the processes they selected for solving the problem and the rationale that supports their answer. Armed with these new insights about student thinking, teachers have the information about student strengths and weaknesses they need to decide what curriculum content is appropriate and what teaching strategies would be effective.

Sample of an Item-Specific Scoring Rubric

The holistic rubric can be modified to meet the specific criteria of each problem, as shown in the sample below. The criteria should be clearly communicated to the students so that they know what needs to be done to meet the specificity of the rubric. Be careful, however. The scoring guide should not dictate one and only one solution strategy.

Choose a Strategy   Use a strategy from the lists to solve the following problem. Explain your choice of strategy.

- Draw a Diagram
- Perform an Experiment
- Guess, Check and revise
- Make a Table

Your suitcase holds 40 pounds. How many 2 pound shirts and how many 5 pound pants can you pack in your case? (5 points)

Rubric for This Item

Level	What to look for
4 or 5 Superior	• The strategy chosen • A restatement of the problem in terms of the solution strategy • More than one solution • Correct computations • Justification for the answers
3 Satisfactory with minor flaws	• The strategy chosen • One correct solution • Nearly all correct computations • Some justification of the answers
1 or 2 Attempted with major flaws	• A strategy, even if it is not complete or does not work • Mostly correct computations • No justification
0 Unsatisfactory	• Any attempt that shows little or no understanding of the problem presented*

* A more constructive approach to unsatisfactory work is to ask the student to rework the problem. This avoids the stigma of a 0 for a grade and gives the student more time to think about his or her response. This usually will produce better scores, but more importantly, will help the student learn how to solve the problem.

Samples of Student Work

Here are four actual student responses to this item with ideas about how to score them.

Your suitcase holds 40 pounds. How many 2 pound shirts and how many 5 pound pants can you pack in your case?

```
    40
   - 7
    33
   - 7
    26      6 pants
   - 7
    19      5 shirts
   - 7
    12
   - 7
    (5)   - 1 pants
  More than one answer

      20
   2)40     20 shirts  0 pants

       8
   5)40     8 pants  0 shirts
```

SCORE: 4 POINTS   The solution shows

- an efficient subtraction process, interpreted in terms of the problem;
- more than one answer, but not all;
- correct computation;
- no justifications for why the process works was included.

[drawing of 10 shirts labeled "2" totaling 20, and 4 pants labeled "5" totaling 20]

10 shirts and 4 pants

SCORE: 3 POINTS   The solution shows

- a pictorial arrangement of one solution;
- an answer in terms of the problem;
- implied computations;
- no justification.

```
      40
      -2      19
      38      -2
      -5      17
      33      -5
      -2      12
      31      -2
      -5      10
      26      -5
      -2       5
      24      -2
      -5       3
      19      -2
               1
```

2 = 7   7 shirts and 5 pants
5 = 5   with 1 lbs to spare

SCORE: 2 POINTS   The solution shows

- a subtraction process for solving;
- an answer in terms of the problem, although the problem was misinterpreted;
- correct computations;
- no justification.

$40 - 5 = 35 - 5 = 30 - 5 = 20 - 2 = 18 - 2 = 16 - 2 = 14$

SCORE: 1 POINT   The solution shows

- an incomplete subtraction process for solving;
- no answer;
- correct computation;
- no justifications.

Sample Solution to the Open-Response Item

Item Your suitcase holds 40 pounds. How many 2 pound shirts and how many 5 pound pants can you pack in your case? (5 points)

Restate the Problem

I need to find how many pants and shirts total 40 pounds.

Select a Strategy

I can make a table showing the number of pants and shirts possible. I want the number of pounds to total 40.

Number of pants	Pounds of pants	Pounds of shirts	Number of shirts	Total pounds, shirts and pants

Solve

Number of pants	Pounds of pants	Pounds of shirts	Number of shirts	Total pounds, shirts and pants
0	0	40	20	0 + 40 = 40
2	10	30	15	10 + 30 = 40
4	20	20	10	20 + 20 = 40
6	30	10	5	30 + 10 = 40
8	40	0	0	40 + 0 = 40

Justify I can only use an even number of pants. When I tried an odd number of pants, I could not use a whole number of shirts to make 40 pounds. Once I decided on the number of pants, I multiplied this number by 5 and subtracted it from 40 to find the pounds of shirts I could take. Then I divided by 2 to get the number of pants. I do not think that 0 shirts or 0 pants are reasonable solutions.

Solution Three solutions are possible: 2 pants with 15 shirts; 4 pants with 10 shirts; and 6 pants with 5 shirts.

Check
$2(5) + 15(2) = 10 + 30 = 40$
$4(5) + 10(2) = 20 + 20 = 40$
$6(5) + 5(2) = 30 + 10 = 40$

All three solutions check.

Caution This is one method for solution. Others are possible. For example, you might assume that it was okay to just have 39 pounds in your suitcase, which would give you four more solutions. Or you might try listing the possibilities, as shown.

$40 - 2(5) = 30;\ 30 \div 2 = 15$ 2 pants with 15 shirts
$40 - 4(5) = 20;\ 20 \div 2 = 10$ 4 pants with 10 shirts
$40 - 6(5) = 10;\ 10 \div 2 = 5$ 6 pants with 5 shirts

Middle School Math, Course 1
Professional Development Book

Generic Scoring Rubric

3-Point Rubric	4-Point Rubric	5-Point Rubric
3 points—Superior	4 points—Superior	5 points—Superior
Student shows thorough understanding of the concept by • using creative, appropriate strategies; • writing clear, complete explanations that include generalizations, examples, or new connections; • providing clear, appropriate charts and graphs; • exceeding the minimum requirements of the problem.		
	3 points—Satisfactory	4 points—Satisfactory
	Student shows clear understanding of the concept by • using appropriate strategies; • writing a clear explanation; • providing appropriate graphs; • satisfying the requirements of the task.	
2 points—Satisfactory, with minor oversights	2 points—Satisfactory, with minor flaws	3 points—Satisfactory, with minor flaws
Student shows understanding of the concept by • using appropriate strategies, although they may not be the most efficient; • writing an explanation that is mainly clear, but may show some gaps; • providing charts and graphs that are mostly clear and appropriate; • completing most elements of the task.		
1 point—Nearly satisfactory, with major flaws	1 point—Nearly satisfactory, with major flaws	2 points—Nearly satisfactory, with major flaws
Student shows a rudimentary understanding of the concept by • choosing inappropriate strategies, or misusing appropriate ones; • calculating correctly most of the time; • writing explanations that are difficult to follow; • providing charts and graphs that are mostly clear and appropriate; • satisfying some elements of the task.		
		1 point—Nearly unsatisfactory
		Student shows little understanding of the concept by • trying to use an inappropriate strategy, but calculating correctly; • writing an explanation that did not connect to the problem or the solution; • satisfying few elements of the task.
0 points—Unsatisfactory	0 points—Unsatisfactory	0 Points—Unsatisfactory
Student shows little understanding of the concept by • not using a recognizable process; • calculating incorrectly; • writing unclear explanations; • using inappropriate charts and graphs; • satisfying no elements of the task.		

Teaching Mathematical Vocabulary

Using the correct vocabulary is a key component of clear communication. When students use the precision and power of math vocabulary, they improve their ability to grasp and share mathematical ideas. Several studies have shown this link between math vocabulary and success in mathematics. It is no surprise, therefore, that the National Council of Teachers of Mathematics states in their *Principles and Standards for School Mathematics* that all instruction through grade 12 should enable students to use the language of mathematics to express mathematical ideas precisely.

Agreeing that math vocabulary is important is just the first step. Teachers also need to learn and apply instructional strategies for successfully acquiring a technical vocabulary, since even the most able students may struggle with the precise language of mathematics. One reason why they may struggle is that math vocabulary and everyday language overlap in complex ways. Researchers have identified three categories for words used in mathematics.

- Words, like *sum*, that have the same meaning in mathematical English as they do in everyday English
- Words, like *cosine*, that have only a mathematical meaning
- Words, like *product*, or *similar*, that have mathematical meanings that are different or more specialized than their everyday English meanings

When a teacher anticipates and addresses the confusion caused by multiple meanings attached to mathematical vocabulary, a student's confusion decreases.

Fostering a Supportive Environment

Acquiring a math vocabulary is an essential skill at all grade levels. In the middle grades, the curriculum and environment have some distinctive features that should guide the instructional approach. First, mathematics is generally more complex and often more abstract than in the lower grades. Every effort should be made to relate new concepts to prior knowledge, to concrete examples, and to real-world applications. Secondly, middle-school students face strong peer pressure; they do not want to stand out, to be different. Students need a classroom setting in which they feel free to express themselves openly, without fear. In this environment, students can try out new ideas and new vocabulary even when the concepts are not fully formed.

Teachers can do much, both in their general approach to teaching and by using specific instructional strategies, to aid math vocabulary acquisition. Some tips for creating and maintaining an environment that fosters communication include the following.

- Provide opportunities for students to speak and listen to mathematics and to reflect on their learning. Involve students in discussions in which they justify solutions or strategies. As students try to convey their ideas, they can develop an appreciation for the need to be precise in the language they use.
- Have students write often. They should write not only to reflect on or to clarify mathematical ideas, but also to internalize new vocabulary words. Include homework writing assignments in which students employ new vocabulary.
- Use familiar language with students as they begin to articulate new math ideas as a foundation for building a connection to formal math language.
- Incorporate new mathematics vocabulary into daily lessons. This allows students, particularly those students acquiring English, to hear the words pronounced and used correctly and in the right context.

- Take advantage of technology as another solid basis for communicating mathematical language. Tools, like calculators and spreadsheets, use expressions that are specific to them. Students can profit from experiences that require them to compare those expressions to related mathematical expressions.

- Have students make math glossaries. Encourage them to include examples and sketches that illustrate the new vocabulary words. Invite students acquiring English to write the words in their native language, as needed. Students can work using the Chapter Review pages of the Notetaking guide.

Using Vocabulary Strategies

Many strategies have been developed to help students learn new vocabulary. These strategies all differ in organization and structure, but they all activate students' prior knowledge about the word. Examples of these structures are shown on the next two pages. These structures include the concept definition map, or the Frayer model, and the semantic, or concept, map.

The Concept Definition Map This structure assumes that many relationships exist between a concept and the knowledge associated with a concept. There are at least four types of associations, and each of these is included on the map. The four relationships are:

- Category: What type of thing is this concept?
- Properties: What attributes define this particular concept?
- Examples: What are some examples of this concept?
- Comparisons: What are some other ways to classify objects in the same category? What things do not belong to this concept but do belong to other members of the same category?

The Semantic Definition Map A semantic definition map has a more open structure than the concept definition map or the Frayer model. It consists of boxes, circles, line segments, and arrows showing ideas related to the main concept, and lists of items within the related concepts. A semantic definition map can be as simple or as complex as the concept dictates. Use these steps for constructing a semantic definition map of a concept.

1. Sketch a framework for the semantic map. Use your students' prior knowledge to decide on the number of boxes that will surround the concept on the map and the name of each box. Preview the heads and bold-faced type in the text that surrounds the concept to decide if additional boxes are needed.

2. Have students read the text. Have them look for key ideas about the concept and any supporting features of the key ideas.

3. Construct the map. Have students fill in the details of the map using the new information from their reading. Additional boxes or lists may be added, as appropriate.

Both general and specific instructional strategies are available to teachers to help foster mathematics vocabulary acquisition. Students need opportunities to see, say, hear, and write the new words correctly. When teachers allow students to read new words, to categorize and compare them, to connect them with their daily lives, to use them precisely when speaking, and to use them in written explanations, then student achievement shows a marked improvement.

Lesson 7.2

Name _____ Date _____

Vocabulary Strategies

Use after Lesson 7.2.

Strategy: Use a Concept Map

Using a concept map can help you gain a fuller understanding of the meaning of a word.

Complete the two maps below for *Simplest Form* and for *Improper Fraction*.

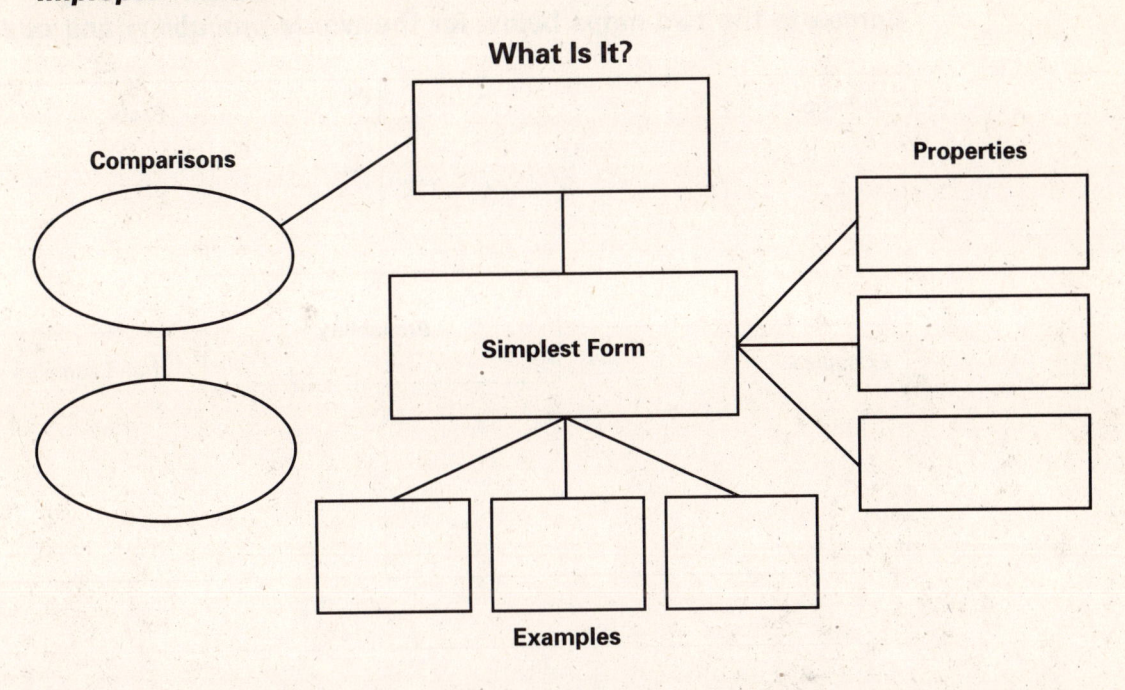

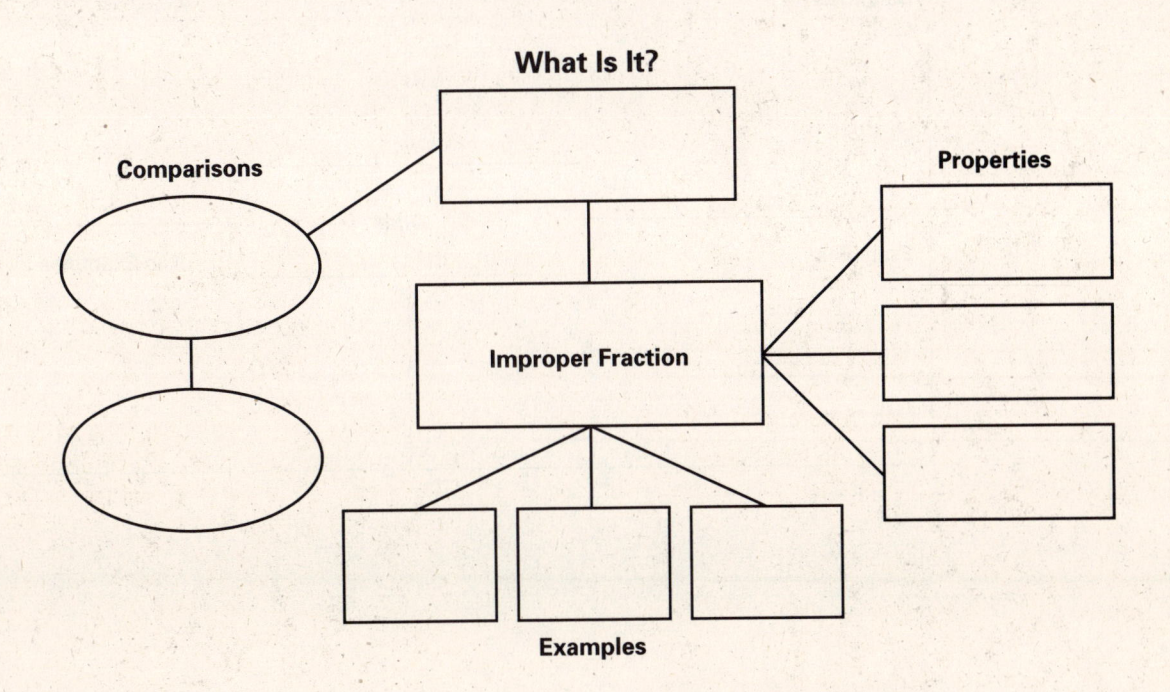

What Is It?

Comparisons

Simplest Form

Properties

Examples

What Is It?

Comparisons

Improper Fraction

Properties

Examples

Middle School Math, Course 1   **15**
Professional Development Book

Lesson 13.1

Name _____ Date _____

Vocabulary Strategies
Use after Lesson 13.1.

Strategy: Use an Idea Web

Knowing the definition of a new math vocabulary word does not necessarily mean that it sticks in your memory. To better understand the meaning of a math vocabulary word, use a spider web to map out the connecting ideas that relate to the new word.

Complete the two maps below for the words *probability* and *odds*.

Definition	Facts
	Probability
Examples	Non-Examples

Definition	Facts
	Odds
Examples	Non-Examples

16 Middle School Math, Course 1
Professional Development Book

Copyright © McDougal Littell Inc.
All rights reserved.

Reading in Math

Teaching middle-school students the strategies for reading mathematics and math textbooks is not about teaching *basic reading skills*. In math, as in other content areas, the focus of teaching reading is to provide students with ways to think and learn about the subject. For example, when students first learn there are "positive and negative numbers," they may chuckle to themselves, thinking, "What are these new types of numbers? If a number has a bad day, does this make it negative?" "Why are these numbers so moody?" Helping students make appropriate connections to the math vocabulary will help them quickly incorporate and apply the new math vocabulary.

Three elements interact to influence how effectively students comprehend the math materials:

- the textbooks themselves,
- the prior knowledge that students bring to the subject, and
- the learning environment of the mathematics classroom.

Supporting Reading in the Content Area

Although math textbooks are designed to guide readers, they need to be read in a different way. Notice the way sentences are structured, the way particular pages are set up, and the way vocabulary is presented and used. Additionally, reading math texts means decoding not only prose, but mathematical symbols, signs, illustrations, graphs, and tables, as well. To confuse matters, some words have more than one meaning, more than one symbol can represent the same idea, and symbols may appear in different orders or positions. When students read math texts, they may not necessarily be reading from left to right and from top to bottom. For example, teachers need to be aware of how very puzzling something like $32 \div 4$, written as $4\overline{)32}$, may look to an inexperienced reader.

While no quick solutions will make math symbols and concepts easy to read for all students, teachers can help students get the most from their texts. Here are some pointers.

- In general, math textbooks contain five kinds of writing: *exposition*, *instructions*, *exercises* and *examples*, *peripheral writing*, and *signals*. Help students recognize and understand each type of writing. Textbook instructions that appear straightforward to you, may be confusing to students because of unfamiliar words or phrases.
- Review the parts of a textbook lesson and of a chapter. Guide students to spot clues for the way lessons and chapters are organized and how information, such as new vocabulary, is presented. Guide them to notice the different graphic elements that identify repeating parts of lessons and features, and those that signal other special pages, such as reviews or tests.
- Assess the sentence structure the text uses. You may wish to adapt some passages to make them more accessible.
- Supplement textbook information with visual and audio aids.
- Math terms are often semantically related to common English words. To help students see how the related words are linked, use a graphic organizer to show these connections. Graphic organizers, appropriately used, can improve students' questioning ability and retention.

- Comprehending word problems can present challenges for students. To help them, you can provide graphic organizers they can use to analyze the problems and then plan their solutions. In a K-N-W-S (Know-Not Needed-What-Strategy) chart, for instance, students record what information the problem provides and does not provide, what the problem asks them to figure out, and what strategies or tools they will use to solve it.

In general, be aware of what students do and do not understand as they read the text. Use appropriate strategies to resolve any comprehension problems. To monitor comprehension, question students. Have them restate troublesome passages in their own words or summarize what a lesson teaches or what a problem asks. Also have students formulate their own questions.

Connecting with Students' Prior Knowledge

Reading in math relies heavily on conceptual understanding. Successful readers build on their prior knowledge; they grasp new concepts because they can relate the new ideas and terms to what they already know. Therefore, it is important to activate students' prior knowledge. When introducing new concepts, verify that students fully comprehend the meaning of previously introduced vocabulary. To help plan what vocabulary or concepts to review before introducing new material, have students fill in a K-W-L (Know-Want to Know-Learned) chart. This graphic organizer has three parts. Students record (1) what they already know about a topic, (2) what they want to find out about it, and (3) what they have learned after reading about it.

Another useful approach is to have brainstorming sessions in which students share what they already know about a topic and identify what they do not know.

Developing a Supportive Learning Environment

The final element that affects how students read mathematics is the learning environment in the math classroom. Some teaching tips and pointers for creating and maintaining an environment that fosters success in reading math are the following.

- Provide an atmosphere in which students can interact comfortably with mathematical ideas. Work to build a sense of community in the middle grades in which students "feel free to express their ideas honestly and openly."
- Provide opportunities for students to write, speak, and listen to learn mathematics and to reflect on their learning. Involve students in small-group discussions in which they justify solutions or strategies or summarize concepts.
- Provide independent reading opportunities that relate to the content you are studying and that use the vocabulary the text introduces. This allows students to see the words in context within a setting that may be more relaxed for them.
- Model your own comprehension strategies. Demonstrate how you "think aloud" while reading new material. Encourage students to reread all or parts of what they are reading.
- Be supportive of partial answers to problems and give credit for the effort students make in expressing math concepts.

Reading in math provides many challenges, but it also provides many opportunities. Using the rich tools available, you can help students become better math readers.

LESSON 6.1

Name _____ Date _____

Reading Math Strategies
Use after Lesson 6.1.

Strategy: Use a K-W-L Chart

How much do you know about estimating with fractions and mixed numbers?

Would you like to be able to find the approximate sum of two fractions mentally? What would you like to know about estimating fractions, their sums and differences?

What have you learned after reading about ways to estimate fraction sums and differences?

Answer the above questions by filling in the K-W-L chart below. First, fill in the top part by explaining what you already know about estimating with fractions and mixed numbers. Then fill in the middle part by writing what you want to know about the topic. Next, fill in the bottom part by describing what you now know after working through the lesson.

Math Topic: _____

K	What Do I *KNOW*?	
W	What Do I *WANT TO KNOW*?	
L	What Have I *LEARNED*?	

Challenge How can my teacher use the information I have provided in the chart?

Middle School Math, Course 1
Professional Development Book

Lesson 12.3

Name _____ Date _____

Reading Math Strategies
Use after Lesson 12.3.

Strategy: Use a K-N-W-S Chart

Sometimes, a math problem can have you at a complete loss. It often helps to step back and take a deep breath. You can also fill in the following chart to help break apart and analyze the problem. The last step in the chart will help you plan how to solve the problem.

Complete the K-N-W-S worksheet below for Lesson _____, Problem _____.

When you have completed the chart, share your responses with classmates. Be ready to justify your strategy decisions.

K What do I *KNOW* from the information the problem provides?	N Which information do I *NOT NEED* to solve the problem?	W *WHAT* does the problem ask me to find?	S What *STRATEGY* will I use to solve the problem? What tools or operations will I use?

Summarize Did filling out this chart help you solve the problem? Explain.

_____

_____

20 **Middle School Math, Course 1**
PROFESSIONAL DEVELOPMENT BOOK

Copyright © McDougal Littell Inc.
All rights reserved.

Teaching Critical Thinking Skills

To think critically means to use a thinking process that helps us make decisions about what to do or believe. In our lives, we routinely find ourselves in situations that are *non-routine*, in which we do not automatically know how to proceed and in which we are uncertain as to the outcome. In these situations, we interpret, analyze, reason, draw conclusions, and make predictions. We also think creatively.

Throughout the educational community, support is widespread for teaching students how to think analytically and creatively. There is also wide agreement that critical thinking skills are not "something extra." Rather, they are basic to the math curriculum and part of daily lessons. The term *critical thinking* is a particularly good one because of the different meanings of *critical*. Critical means *analytical*, *judicious*, and *evaluative*. It also means *vital* and *indispensable*. Indeed, the teaching of critical thinking skills is indispensable to any mathematics program.

The *National Council of Teachers of Mathematics* affirms that reasoning is integral to doing mathematics and should therefore be interwoven throughout the math curriculum from pre-kindergarten through grade 12. In The *Principles and Standards for School Mathematics*, the council states that

> . . . students should enter the middle grades with the view that math involves examining patterns and noting regularities, making conjectures about possible generalizations, and evaluating the conjectures. In grades 6–8, students should sharpen and extend their reasoning skills by deepening their evaluations of their assertions and conjectures using inductive and deductive reasoning to formulate mathematical arguments.

Identifying Critical Thinking Skills

Students should learn to use inductive reasoning to search for mathematical relationships through the examination of patterns. Consider this example:

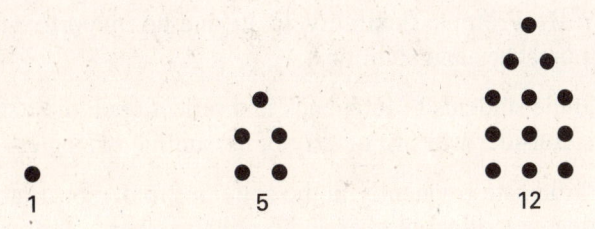

What are the fifth and sixth pentagonal numbers?

Some students may draw diagrams to find the answers: 35 and 51. Others may find the pattern of differences between successive pentagonal numbers and then extend the pattern of differences. [+4, +7, +10, +13, +16 . . .]

Math educators have identified a number of critical thinking skills that help students solve nonroutine problems like the one above. With guidance all students can learn and use the following creative and thoughtful approaches, in various combinations, to attack problems.

Explain	Look for a Pattern
Describe	Make a Prediction
Compare and Contrast	Use Logic
Choose a Method	Interpret
Choose an Operation	Draw a Conclusion

Making Critical Thinking a Daily Event

As teachers, much can be done to make critical thinking an integral part of mathematics instruction. Here are some tips that help students develop their critical thinking and problem solving skills.

- Present the kinds of activities that provide students opportunities to work through situations that require critical thinking—those in which they make comparisons and conjectures, estimate reasonable results, draw conclusions, make predictions, use logical reasoning, look for patterns, and decide what to do using given information.

- Use thought-provoking questions. Ask *Why? How? What if?*

- Provide time for students to consider questions fully before responding; this can involve days, perhaps weeks.

- Promote open discussions in small groups where students can observe how others think, and where they can share and explain their struggles, strategies, triumphs, and solutions.

- Allow students to think out loud.

- Choose problems that engage students' interest and that reflect their expanding math understanding, skills, and language.

- Many students need to experience repeated success in order to see themselves as successful problem solvers. To aid success, on occasion select problems that are just a little easier than average.

- Have whole-class discussions in which students brainstorm possible approaches and solution strategies.

- Guide students to understand that there is often more than one correct answer and more than one way to solve a problem.

- Foster a classroom environment that encourages students to express their ideas freely. Promote flexibility. Invite and be supportive of creative, divergent approaches and solutions.

- Guide students to look back and reflect upon their strategies. Ask them to consider ways to modify or streamline strategies.

- Participate frequently in the activities to demonstrate that you, too, are a creative critical thinker and problem solver.

Students with good critical thinking skills will think more creatively. They will become better able to analyze, reason, and interpret facts. They will become better decision makers and problem solvers. And, they will develop a more positive disposition toward mathematics as they experience its power and usefulness.

LESSON 5.4

Name _____ Date _____

Critical Thinking Skills
Use after Lesson 5.4.

Numbers That Go Together

Look at the numbers in each shape. Write what the numbers within the shape have in common.

1. (diamond shape containing: 257, 224, 404, 819, 167)

    _____
    _____

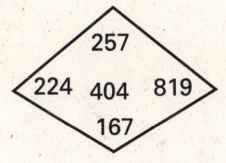

2. (pentagon containing: 135, 216, 81, 936, 225)

    _____
    _____

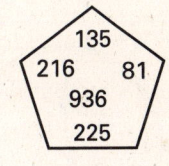

3. (parallelogram containing: 184, 280, 264, 984, 96)

    _____
    _____

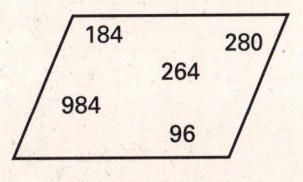

4. (triangle containing: 27, 125, 343, 512, 8)

    _____
    _____

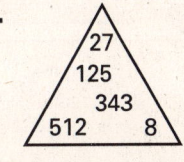

Use the following information to solve Exercise 5. Work together with a classmate.

Each of these sets of numbers is a *snorg:*

   {11, 13, 17}   {47, 53, 59}   {73, 79, 83}   {37, 41, 43}

Each of these sets of numbers is *not a snorg:*

   {3, 5, 7}   {43, 44, 45}   {78, 80, 81}   {19, 23, 29, 31}

Make a list of anything you notice about *snorgs.*

_____   _____
_____   _____
_____   _____

Make a list of anything you notice about the *not-a-snorgs.*

_____   _____
_____   _____
_____   _____

5. Explain what you think a *snorg* is. _____
   _____

6. Make up your own *snorg.* _____
   _____

Copyright © McDougal Littell Inc.
All rights reserved.

Middle School Math, Course 1
Professional Development Book

Lesson 11.7

Name _____ Date _____

Critical Thinking Skills
Use after Lesson 11.7.

Do You Have the Time?

Look at the clocks. Each is a mirror reflection. Write the actual time it is for each clock.

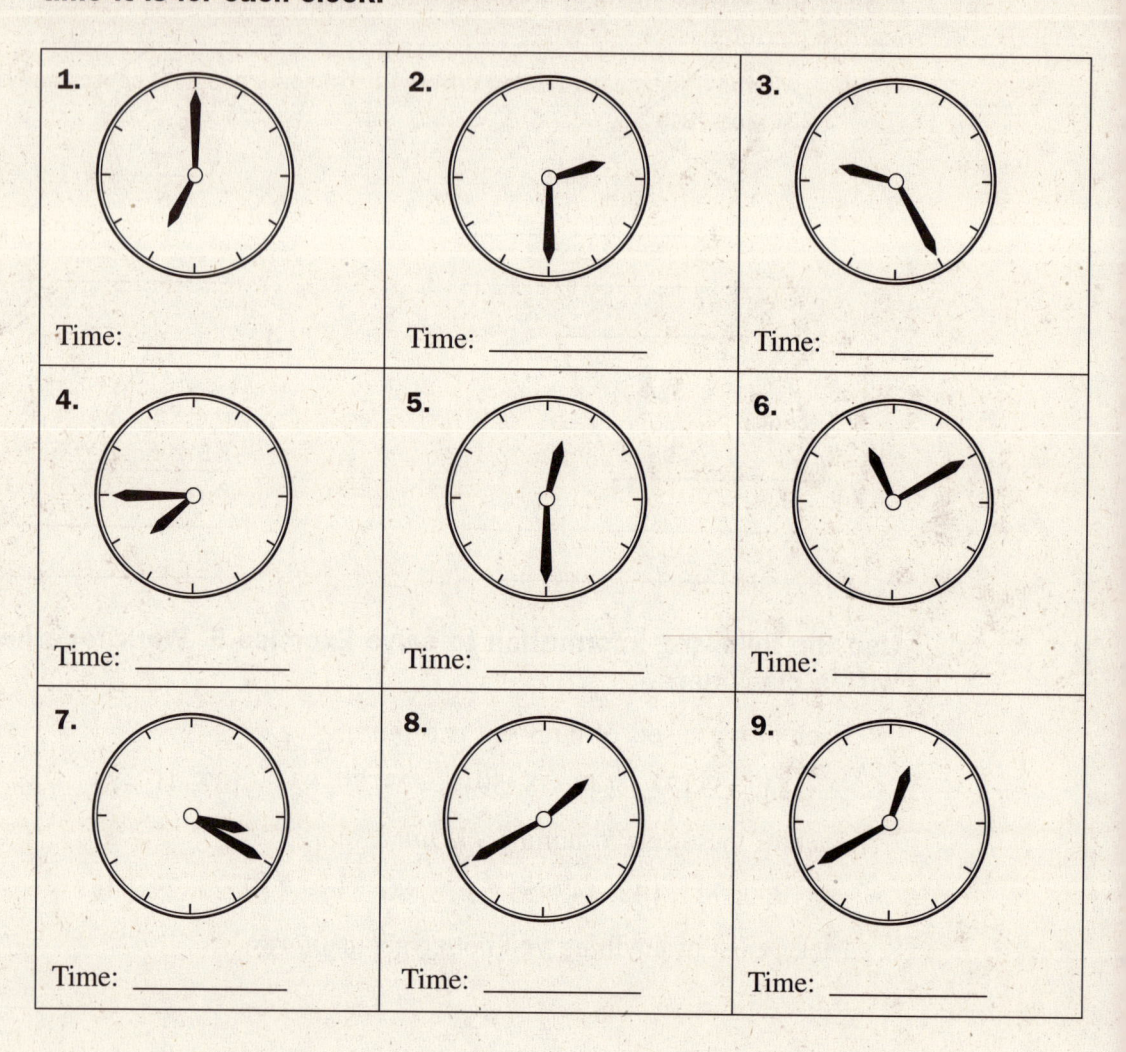

1. Time: _____

2. Time: _____

3. Time: _____

4. Time: _____

5. Time: _____

6. Time: _____

7. Time: _____

8. Time: _____

9. Time: _____

10. Describe the strategy or strategies you used to find the actual times.

_____
_____
_____

Middle School Math, Course 1
Professional Development Book

Copyright © McDougal Littell Inc.
All rights reserved.

Teaching Problem Solving Strategies

People engage in problem solving all the time; it is part of everyday life. It is the technique we employ to remove obstacles between us and something we want. Often when a problem first presents itself, we do not know what needs to be done or even where to begin. We do know, however, that we cannot let the obstacles stand in the way. Instead, we need to tackle the problem in an organized way, working until a method of solution is found. The scope of the problem is irrelevant. It can be as monumental as determining how to eradicate poverty or as small as figuring out where a pair of glasses was left.

Problem solving affects each person differently. In some people it causes anxiety and frustration; in others it creates a sense of delight at the prospect of thinking creatively. Solving problems can also be a source of relaxation. In any case, the more people engage in problem solving, the more skilled and successful they become. This is also true for students.

Weaving Problem Solving into Every Lesson

The National Council of Teachers of Mathematics and other curriculum leaders agree that problem solving is a key goal of mathematics teaching and that it should be interwoven throughout the mathematics curriculum to provide a context for learning and applying mathematical ideas. According to NCTM's *Principles and Standards for School Mathematics*, all instructional programs through grade 12 should enable students to—

- build new mathematical knowledge through problem solving;
- solve problems that arise in mathematics and in other contexts;
- apply and adapt a variety of appropriate strategies to solve problems;
- monitor and reflect on the process of mathematical problem solving.

Problem solving approaches and strategies can be taught. You can guide students to learn and use productive methods to attack problems. Start by emphasizing the four-step process for solving problems, introduced on page 42 of the text. This four-step process is as valid today as it was when George Polya introduced it in his book *How to Solve It* nearly 60 years ago. These steps are:

(1) Read and understand.

(2) Make a plan.

(3) Solve the problem.

(4) Look back.

Utilizing the four-step approach to problem solving is an essential component in the development of successful problem solvers. Understanding these four steps is the point at which students should begin.

The following list of strategies can be used for solving widely dissimilar problems with varying degrees of difficulty and complexity. Using them can make problems clearer, simpler, and more manageable.

Guess, Check, and Revise	Look for a Pattern
Act It Out	Draw a Diagram
Make a Table	Solve a Simpler Problem
Work Backward	Solve a Related Problem
Make a Model	Use an Equation
Make a List	Break into Parts
Draw a Graph	Perform an Experiment

As teachers, you can make problem solving an integral part of mathematics instruction and thereby contribute toward a positive environment in which to learn mathematics. Here are some pointers.

- Provide many experiences in nonroutine problem solving. Allow frequent opportunities for both independent and collaborative problem solving experiences.

- Choose problems carefully. You want the problems to help students deepen their understanding of key math concepts and to engage their interest. Problems should also reflect your students' expanding math understanding, skills, and language. Some problems should be done over time, and some problems should contain extraneous or insufficient information.

- Encourage flexibility in the solution process. Invite creative approaches and solutions. Allow students to choose appropriate and effective strategies. Encourage multiple-solution strategies for problems and a no-one-way-is-best approach by students.

- Communication is the key. Have students share and explain their strategies and solutions. Encourage students to give complete solutions. Guide students in looking back and reflecting upon their strategies for ways to modify, or streamline, them. Have students choose and formulate their own problems utilizing a variety of situations.

- Model the problem solving plan in your teaching. Articulate your reasoning as you resolve difficult problems in the classroom. This will demonstrate that you, too, are a problem solver.

The *Principles and Standards for School Mathematics* states that through problem solving, "students can experience the power and utility of mathematics." Make problem solving integral to your math curriculum.

Lesson 1.2

Strategies for Problem Solving
Use after Lesson 1.1.

Strategy: Drawing a Diagram

Some mathematical problems involve a physical situation. When they do, drawing a diagram or a picture can help you better understand them and to come up with a plan for solving them.

Problem

Five structures are still standing in Ghost Town State Park. Two dirt roads start at the schoolhouse. One goes to the jail, and the other one goes to the corral. One road goes from the jail to the mine, and another links the corral with the mine. There is also a road from the corral to the jail.

How many ways can you travel from the schoolhouse to the mine?

Solution

Read and Understand   Six roads are on a map. You need to find how many routes lead from the schoolhouse to the mine using the six roads.

Make a Plan   Make a drawing of the routes. Trace, and then list, the routes from the schoolhouse to the mine.

Solve the Problem   Here is one possible diagram. You can get to the mine by first going past the jail, or by first going past the corral. So, four routes are possible.

- schoolhouse → jail → mine
- schoolhouse → jail → corral → mine
- schoolhouse → corral → mine
- schoolhouse → corral → jail → mine

Look Back   No other routes seem reasonable.

Draw a diagram to solve.

1. A train links these towns: Alton and Dawson; Dawson, Brady and Colby, Emory and Colby; and Dawson and Emory. How many ways could you travel from Emory to Brady?

2. Luis, Marcel, Noemi, and Yumi play chess. Each person will play the other three once. How many games will they play in all? Suppose Pat joins in and plays all the others. Now how many games will be played?

3. A pool is 40 feet long and 25 feet wide. A cement strip, 5 feet wide, goes around the edge of the pool, and a fence runs along the outer perimeter of the strip. How long is the fence?

4. *Writing*   Make up a problem that can best be solved by drawing a diagram. First, solve it yourself. Then challenge a classmate to solve it.

Lesson 7.7 Strategies for Problem Solving

Use after Lesson 7.7.

Problem

There are 64 soccer teams in a single-elimination tournament. Each team plays until it loses. How many games will be played?

Solution

Read and Understand You know how many teams are in the tournament, and that a team is eliminated when it loses. You need to figure out how many games must be played to eliminate all teams but one.

Make a Plan When a problem has large numbers, it is helpful to first solve the same problem using smaller numbers. In this case, try tournament with 2 teams, then 4 teams, and then 8 teams.

Solve the Problem Here is how to use a simpler problem.

Think: Begin with two teams: A and B. How many games played?	A plays B. One winner. So, 2 teams = 1 game.
Think: Try four teams: A, B, C, and D. How many games played?	A plays B. C plays D. The winners of the two games play. So, 4 teams = 3 games.
Think: Try eight teams: A, B, C, D, E, F, G, and H. How many games played?	A plays B = winner 1. C plays D = winner 2. E plays F = winner 3. G plays H = winner 4. So, 4 games are played. Now the 4 winning teams play 2 games. Winner 1 plays winner 2. Winner 3 plays winner 4. The winners of the two games play 1 final game. Total the number of games played: 4 + 2 + 1 = 7 games. So, 8 teams = 7 games.

Notice that the number of games played is always *one less* than the number of teams entered. In a 64-team single-elimination tournament, there will be 63 games played in order to determine the champion.

Look Back The answer makes sense because for a team to win a tournament, every other team must lose. There will be as many games as there are losing teams.

Use a simpler problem to solve.

1. There were 20 Democrats and 20 Republicans at a meeting. Each Democrat shook hands with each Republican once. How many handshakes were there?

2. Rosa is cutting a long chain into small equal-sized pieces to make 20 bracelets. How many cuts does she need to make?

CHAPTER 1: Math Behind the Math

Use with Chapter 1.

Lesson 1.1

PLACE VALUE In the ninth century, a mathematician and astronomer named al-Khawarizmi integrated mathematical knowledge from Greece and India. He popularized the use of Arabic numerals 0–9 and the base-ten place-value system that we use to read, write, and calculate numbers. Al-Khawarizmi formalized many of the rules we use in mathematics today. Our word *algorithm* is derived from his name, and *algebra* is from the name of one of his books. Understanding this place-value structure is the foundation on which the arithmetic computations for addition, subtraction, multiplication, and division are based.

In whole-number place value, each successive place to the left is ten times greater than the place to its right. As a result, regrouping in a computation, such as addition or subtraction, merely shifts equivalent groups of ten from one place to the next in such a way that the quantities retain their value. It is this structure of place value that allows us the shortcut of recording partial products when multiplying or dividing. An illustration of this process is shown in Example 3 on page 6.

Hundreds	**Tens**	Ones
	2	5
×	1	2
	5	0
2	5	
3	0	0

The boldfaced type illustrates the multiplication of 1 ten × 25, which equals the partial product of 25 tens or 250.

The partial product is aligned with the tens place because 2 hundreds + 5 tens = 250.

Lesson 1.2

ROUNDING AND COMPATIBLE NUMBERS
For many problems encountered in daily life, a reasonable estimate is all that is needed. Estimating before computing provides a reasonable target expectation for the solution. Estimating following computing provides a check for the reasonableness of an answer.

When students estimate, ask them to look for two things: a way to make the numbers easy to calculate mentally and an estimate that is accurate for the purpose.

Rounding is one way to make numbers easy to compute mentally. Choosing which place value to round to is a crucial element in determining the accuracy of an estimate. For example, rounding the number 1549 to the nearest ten, hundred, and thousand provides vastly different estimates.

1549 to the nearest ten $\longrightarrow$ 1550
1549 to the nearest hundred $\longrightarrow$ 1500
1549 to the nearest thousand $\longrightarrow$ 2000

Remind students that rounding when multiplying or dividing can lead to estimates that overstate or understate the actual result significantly, especially when both numbers are rounded up or both are rounded down. Consider the following example.

$459 \times 26 = 11,934$

When both factors are rounded to the leading digit, the value of the product is greatly increased.

$500 \times 30 = 15,000$

Since multiplication is repeated addition, and division is repeated subtraction, each repetition of the addition or subtraction exaggerates the estimate.

Estimating quotients using compatible numbers makes computation easier because the process relies on a recall of basic facts. For example, for $652 \div 79$, round 79 to 80. The first few multiples of 8 are 8, 16, 24, 32, 40, 48, 56, 64, and 72. For $652 \div 79$, the basic fact that $64 \div 8 = 8$ leads to the compatible numbers $640 \div 80$. An estimated quotient of 8 is reasonable.

Lesson 1.3

POWERS Writing numbers as *powers* is a shorthand way of writing repeated factors. Powers are used to show extremely great numbers such as astronomical distances. For example, the distance from Earth to the Andromeda Galaxy is calculated to be 2,300,000 or 2.3×10^6 light-years. In scientific notation, the first number is the base (2.3). This first number is always a number less than ten. The second number is written as 10 to the nth power (10^6). Scientific notation collapses base-ten place-value notation so that people can easily read these extremely large numbers.

Middle School Math, Course 1
Professional Development Book
29

Powers can also help to explain two-dimensional or three-dimensional measures such as area and volume. For example:

The area of the floor is 8 ft × 8 ft, or 8^2 square feet.
The volume of the box is 8 in. × 8 in. × 8 in. or 8^3 cubic inches.

To help students visualize powers, draw a square on the board and label each side *s*. Guide students to see that the formula for the area of a square is s^2 because the length of one side is multiplied by itself, or "squared." Then assign a value for *s*, such as 4. Next, have students use calculators to find successively greater powers of the same number (4^2, 4^3, 4^4, 4^5, and 4^6). Help students see that exponential growth ($4^6 = 4096$) is vastly different than multiplication ($4 \times 6 = 24$).

Lessons 1.4–1.6

VARIABLES, EXPRESSIONS, AND EQUATIONS

Just as the numerals 0–9 are the essential building blocks of our place-value system, *variables*, *expressions*, and *equations* are the building blocks of algebra.

An *expression* is a mathematical string that contains some or all of the following: numbers, variables, and operation symbols. Here are some examples of expressions.

$$2 \quad x \quad 3+7 \quad 5-y \quad (3+2) \times 4^4$$

An expression, such as $6(4 + 8)$, is a *numerical expression* because it only contains numbers and represents a particular value, in this case, 72.

Expressions such as $a(4 + 8)$ or $a(b + c)$ are called *variable expressions*. *Variables* are the letters that represent given values.

In a *variable expression*, the value of the expression changes depending on the value assigned to the variable. For example, in $a(4 + 8)$, the value of the expression is equal to 24, 60, or 96 when $a = 2, 5,$ or 8.

To *evaluate an expression*, you replace each occurrence of the variable with its assigned value. Then you *simplify the expression* using the usual rules for the order of operations: parentheses first, then powers, multiply and divide from left to right, then add and subtract from left to right.

An *equation* is a mathematical statement that joins two expressions together with an equals sign. Here are some examples of equations.

$$4 = 4 \quad 14 = 2 + 12 \quad s + 5 = 7 \quad 1 \cdot b = b$$

To *solve an equation* that has a variable, you must find the number or numbers that when substituted for the variable makes the equation true. Each of these values is a *solution*. An equation can have no solution, one solution, or many solutions. For example, the equation $1 \cdot b = b$ has many solutions because the equation is true for any real number value of *b*, but the equation $t + 5 = 7$ has only one solution, 2.

In Chapter 12, students will learn how to formally solve equations by applying inverse operations to both sides of an equation.

Lesson 1.7

A PROBLEM SOLVING PLAN
Regardless of whether the problem to be solved is a mathematical problem or a problem in a student's real life, students must first understand the problem and then identify a plan for solving it. With practice, they can learn the critical thinking skills required to reach an effective solution. These skills include determining the question to be resolved, determining the information that is provided, formulating a realistic plan for the solution process, and checking that the solution obtained meets the criteria of the problem. These skills will allow students to efficiently solve problems within the mathematics classroom and in their lives outside the classroom.

CHAPTER 1

Tips for New Teachers
Use with Chapter 1.

Lesson 1.1

INCLUSION For students who need additional work with multi-digit multiplication, have them write Example 3 on page 6 in the following format. Then have them complete the table.

×	20	5	25
10			
2			
			?

×	20	5	25
10	200	50	250
2	40	10	50
			?

Using this table format helps students to organize their work and also allows you to quickly diagnose problems.

COMMON ERROR Some students may forget to write zeros in a quotient. For example, the quotient for 4910 ÷ 7 is 701 R3. A common error is for students to lose track of place value and write 4910 ÷ 7 as 71 R3. Consider teaching this strategy for remembering place value.

Step 1	Because 7 is greater than 4, write an x above the 4. Write dashes for the remaining place values.
Step 2	Divide 49 by 7. Multiply: 7 × 7 = 49. Write 7 in the quotient. Subtract and bring down.
Step 3	Because 7 is greater than 1, you cannot divide this place. Write a 0 above the 1 in the tens place.
Step 4	Divide 10 by 7. Multiply: 7 × 1 = 7. Write 1 in the quotient. Subtract: 10 − 7 = 3. Write the remainder.

Remind students that once the first digit in the quotient is placed, they must write one digit of the quotient above each remaining digit of the divisor.

Hands-on Activity 1.2

INCLUSION To foster communication skills and critical thinking skills, ask students to verbalize their strategy for winning the "Hitting the Target" addition game after they have played it. Doing so will help students learn to make generalizations and to communicate them to others. Ask students to do the same for the other versions of the game.

Lesson 1.2

TEACHING TIP Sometimes students are confused about what place value to round to when making addition or subtraction estimates. For example, have students consider the sentence 1439 + 168 = 1607. To estimate the sum, have students consider what is reasonable. If they round to the nearest thousand, the estimate is 1000 + 0, or 1000. This is not reasonable, since the sum is less than either addend. Rounding to the nearest hundred, the estimate is 1400 + 200, or 1600, which is reasonable. If students round to the nearest ten, the estimate is 1440 + 170, or 1610. This estimate is close to the actual answer, but since these numbers are not easy to add mentally, rounding to the nearest hundred makes the most sense.

INCLUSION For students that may not be familiar with the word *compatible*, relate the word to friendship. Suggest that "compatible friends" get along well and work well together. When estimating quotients, *compatible numbers* are a divisor and dividend that work well together and result in a reasonable estimate.

Lesson 1.3

INCLUSION Some students may be confused by a sentence such as the following.

Sixteen is two to the fourth power.

When they see *fourth power*, they think that a power is an exponent. To dispel this notion, explain that *two to the fourth power* means *the power, two to the fourth*.

Middle School Math, Course 1   31
Professional Development Book

CHAPTER 1 Continued

Tips for New Teachers
Use with Chapter 1.

Another common usage of the word *power* is Sixteen is a power of both two and of four.

Have students notice that here *power* refers to the value of the exponential expression, not just its exponential form. Another example of this is in Lesson 4.5, in which the numbers 10, 100, and 1000 are referred to as powers of 10.

Lesson 1.4

COMMON ERROR Many students think they can "distribute" an exponent, as in $(3 + 4)^2 = 3^2 + 4^2$. Have students carefully evaluate each of these expressions using the order of operations to see that this is not the case.

$$(3 + 4)^2 = 7^2 = 49$$
$$3^2 + 4^2 = 9 + 16 = 25$$

TEACHING TIP Not all calculators are programmed in the same manner. Have students check their calculators to see which order of operations their calculators use. Have them input the expression $19 - 6 \times 2$. If the display reads 7, the calculator automatically uses the standard order of operations. If the display reads 26, the calculator evaluates expressions from left to right. In this case, to ensure a correct answer students will need to insert parentheses into expressions containing more than one operation. Usually, only the simplest four-function calculators use a left-to-right order.

Hands-on Activity 1.5

TEACHING TIP This is the first time that students have used expressions with more than one operation. Remind students that once they substitute a value for the question mark, they must evaluate the expression using the order of operations, just as they did in Lesson 1.4.

Lesson 1.5

TEACHING TIP Students know they can represent the distance that a car traveled at 65 mi/h for 2 hours as 65×2. The strength of a *variable expression* is that it can represent the distance that a car traveled at 65 mi/h for any number of hours.

Many distances can be represented with only one expression. For example, when h represents number of hours, you can write $65 \cdot h$ or $65h$.

TEACHING TIP To help students understand naming conventions for variables, tell them that any letter of the alphabet can be used as a *variable*, but often the first letter of the object it represents makes sense. Until instructed otherwise, ask students to establish the habit of writing each variable in lowercase. Some letters, such as o, l, and s, should be avoided because they are easily confused with the numbers 0, 1, and 5. For the same reason, the times sign ($\times$) is rarely used in algebra because it is easily confused with the variable x.

Lesson 1.6

INCLUSION The difference between expressions and equations may not be clear to all students, since both may contain variables. In a variable expression, substituting any number for the variable results in a meaningful conclusion. An *equation* is a mathematical sentence formed by placing an equals sign between two expressions. Recall that the following are examples of expressions.

$$3 \quad z \quad 2m \quad 2 + 5 \quad (2 - b) + 6$$

Using the definition of equation, the following are some examples of equations.

$$3 = 3 \quad 2 + 5 = (2 - b) + 6 \quad 2m = z$$

TEACHING TIP Remind students that an equation need not have only one solution, although in introductory work in algebra this is often the case. Have them consider the equation $x + x = 4x \div 2$, which has an infinite number of solutions, and the equation $x \div 0 = 4$, which has no solution.

Lesson 1.7

TEACHING TIP Ask students to look at the diagram and solution for Example 3 on page 43. Specify that for this problem, because all three landmarks lie on the same route, the linear diagram ensures that there is only one solution. The diagram could have an infinite number of solutions if the landmarks were not on the same line of travel.

Chapter 1

Parents as Partners
Use with Chapter 1.

Name _____ Date _____

Chapter Overview One way you can help your student succeed in Chapter 1 is by discussing the lesson goals in the chart below. When a lesson is completed, ask your student the following questions. "What were the goals of the lesson? What new words and formulas did you learn? How can you apply the ideas of the lesson to your life?"

Lesson Title	Lesson Goals	Key Applications
1.1: Whole Number Operations	Add, subtract, multiply, and divide whole numbers. Find patterns in lists of whole numbers.	• Music Lessons • Summer Olympics • Shopping • Traveling
1.2: Whole Number Estimation	Round to estimate sums, differences, products, and quotients of whole numbers.	• Biking • School Carnival • Population • Painting
1.3: Powers and Exponents	Write and find values of powers. Use powers in real-world problems.	• Telephone Calls • Classroom Seating • Invitations • Tiling
1.4: Order of Operations	Evaluate expressions using the order of operations. Solve multi-step problems.	• Aquarium • Gifts • Band Competition
1.5: Variables and Expressions	Evaluate expressions that involve variables.	• Dog Years • Weather • Rafting
1.6: Equations and Mental Math	Solve equations using mental math. Apply rules for operations involving 0 and 1 when using mental math.	• Salmon Migration • Home Run Totals • Computer Games • Baby-sitting • Volleyball
1.7: A Problem Solving Plan	Use a problem solving plan along with various problem solving strategies to solve problems.	• Spending Money • Fencing • Toll Booths • Video Games • Access Codes

Know How to Take Notes

Keeping A Notebook is the strategy featured in Chapter 1 (see page 4). Be sure that your student has set up a notebook for keeping math notes. Encourage your student to keep notebooks up-to-date, so previous lessons can be related to new situations. These notes can be used to share with you what was done in class as well as to study for tests and quizzes.

CHAPTER 1 Continued

Name _____ **Date** _____

Parents as Partners

Use with Chapter 1.

Key Ideas Your student can demonstrate understanding of key concepts by working through the following exercises with you.

Lesson	Exercise
1.1	If you attend 7 classes at school each day and each class is 45 minutes long, how many minutes are you in class during an 180-day school year? How many hours?
1.2	Your dad pays you $9 each time you mow the lawn. If you're trying to earn enough money for a new video game that costs $57, estimate how many times you will have to mow the lawn. Does your estimate give you enough money?
1.3	Write the power as a product. Find its value. (a) 3^4 (b) 7^3 (c) 10^4 (d) 4^6
1.4	Evaluate the expression using the order of operations. (a) $2 \cdot (3 + 4) - 2 \cdot 3 + 4$ (b) $2 \cdot 3 + 4 - 12 \div 2 + 4$
1.5	Evaluate the expression when $x = 5$ and $y = 7$. (a) $6x + 4y$ (b) $5x - y$ (c) $10 \div x + y$ (d) $x^2 + y^2$
1.6	Your family is going on a 17-mile weekend hiking trip. After the first day you have hiked 6 miles. Use mental math to solve the equation $d + 6 = 17$ to find the distance d, in miles, you have left to hike.
1.7	Use the four steps of the problem-solving plan to solve the following problem. Team A scored 2 three-point shots, 6 two-point baskets and 5 free-throws worth one point each. Team B scored 1 three-point shot, 9 two-point baskets and 4 free-throws worth one point each. What was the final score of the basketball game? Which team won?

Home Involvement Activity

Directions: Record separately the number of calories you eat for breakfast, lunch, and dinner during one day. During which meal do you eat the most calories? During which meal do you eat the least number of calories? Using the amounts you found, estimate how many calories you eat each week for breakfast, lunch, and dinner. You can also estimate the total number of calories you eat each week.

Answers: **1.1:** 56,700 minutes; 945 hours. **1.2:** $60 \div 10 = 6$, No, it's not enough money (You'd actually need to mow the lawn 7 times.) **1.3:** (a) 81 (b) 343 (c) 10,000 (d) 4096 **1.4:** (a) 12 (b) 8 **1.5:** (a) 58 (b) 18 (c) 9 (d) 74 **1.6:** $d = 11$ **1.7:** Team A: 23 points; Team B: 25 points; Winner: Team B

Bulletin Board Idea

Use with Chapter 1.

Objective

To visually reinforce the concepts of powers and exponents.

Materials

- yarn
- 4 pads of sticky notes (1.5 in. by 2 in.)
- 64 index cards (3 in. by 5 in.)
- 16 sheets of construction paper (8.5 in. by 11 in.), preferably of the same color
- 2 sentence strips

Constructing the Bulletin Board

1. Using the yarn, divide the bulletin board in half horizontally and then in half vertically.

2. Place four sticky notes on each of the index cards so that all four sticky notes show distinctly. Attach four of these index cards to each sheet of construction paper. Again, be sure all four index cards show distinctly. Now put four of these sheets of construction paper in each quadrant of the bulletin board.

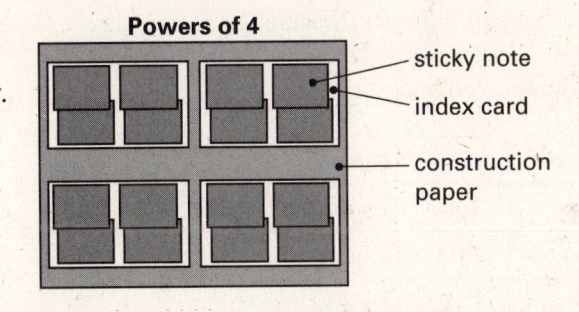

3. On one sentence strip, write the title of the bulletin board "Powers of 4." On the other sentence strip, write "How fast do the powers of 4 grow?" Attach these wherever appropriate on the bulletin board.

Using the Bulletin Board

After students complete Lesson 1.3, discuss the bulletin board and its questions with the class. The discussion may include the following.

- Ask students how many sheets of construction paper and how many index cards are on the board. (4^2 and 4^3) How many stickies are on the board? (4^4)
- Suppose you divide each sticky note into quarters and and draw four dots in each quarter. How many quarters would there be in all? (4^5) How many dots in all? (4^6)
- How much greater is 4^6 than 4×6? (4072)

Follow-up

- Have students make their own illustration of a power. Suggest that they use a small whole number other than 4. Give each student a larger sheet of paper and have them create powers, such as the powers of 4 shown on the bulletin board.

CHAPTER 2
Math Behind the Math
Use with Chapter 2.

Lesson 2.1

CUSTOMARY AND METRIC MEASURES The system of measurement used in the United States is called the *customary*, or English, system. It was formalized in England around the eleventh century. England has since officially dropped this system of measurement. The United States is the only major country in the world that still uses it. Customary units of length include the inch, foot, yard, and mile.

The metric system of measurement was developed in France in the 1790s. This system aligns measurement with the decimal place-value system. The basic unit of length, the meter, is the unit to which all other length units relate. A system of standard prefixes was adopted to show the 10-to-1 relationships between the units. Students may know some metric prefixes because of their use in computer technology.

Prefix	Meaning
kilo-	1000 (1 thousand)
hecto-	100 (1 hundred)
deka-	10 (1 ten)
1 basic unit (meter, liter, gram)	
deci-	0.1 (1 tenth)
centi-	0.01 (1 hundredth)
milli-	0.001 (1 thousandth)

Lesson 2.2

PERIMETER AND AREA *Perimeter* is the distance around a figure. *Area* is the amount of surface the figure covers. To measure the perimeter of any polygon, add the lengths of the sides. Rectangles are polygons that have two pairs of congruent sides. That is why you can use the formula $P = 2\ell + 2w$ to find the perimeter of a rectangle. P represents its perimeter, ℓ represents its length, and w represents its width. Another form of the formula that students may use is $P = 2(\ell + w)$.

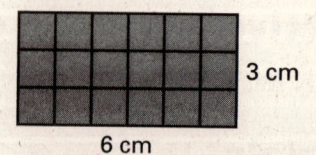

$P = 2\ell + 2w \longrightarrow P = 2(6) + 2(3) = 12 + 6 = 18$ cm
$P = 2(\ell + w) \longrightarrow P = 2(6 + 3) = 2(9) = 18$ cm

The perimeter of a square, like the perimeter of any regular polygon, can be found by multiplying the length of one side by the number of congruent sides. Thus, the formula for the perimeter of a square is $P = 4s$.

Area measure applies only to closed figures that lie in a plane. To find the area of such a figure, determine how many square units cover the surface. For a rectangle, count the number of square units or multiply its length by its width. A square inch is a square that is 1 inch long by 1 inch wide. A square unit has side lengths of one unit, whether the unit is a foot, millimeter, inch, meter, or another unit.

The formula for finding the area of any rectangle is $A = \ell w$. A represents its area, ℓ represents its length, and w represents its width.

Show students how to find unknown measures by writing related equations.

$A = 20$ square inches; $\ell = 10$ inches; $w = ?$ inches

$A = \ell w$
$20 = 10 \cdot w$ ← Use mental math to write $20 = 10 \cdot w$ as
$w = 20 \div 10$ the related equation
$w = 2$ $w = 20 \div 10$.

Lesson 2.3

PROPORTIONAL REASONING A ratio is a comparison of two quantities that uses division. Both quantities are measured in the same unit. For example, to make purple paint, you mix 3 cups red paint with 4 cups blue paint. In mathematics you can write ratios such as this one in words, with symbols, or as fractions.

3 cups to 4 cups   3 : 4 $\frac{3}{4}$

In the red-paint-to-blue-paint example above, notice that 3 cups red paint plus 4 cups blue paint makes 7 cups of paint. If you double the recipe to

Middle School Math, Course 1
Professional Development Book

CHAPTER 2 Continued

Math Behind the Math

Use with Chapter 2.

6 cups red paint and 8 cups blue paint, you now have 14 cups of purple paint. The ratios 3 : 4 and 6 : 8 are equivalent ratios. You have more paint, but the relationship between the quantities of blue and red paint remains the same.

In this lesson, students use informal algebraic thinking to write equivalent ratios for their scale drawings. Two equivalent ratios separated by an equals sign are called a proportion.

Multiplying each term in the ratio by the same number produces an equivalent ratio.

Lessons 2.4–2.7

CHOOSING THE APPROPRIATE GRAPH Students should understand that there is not one all-purpose graphical representation that can be used for every purpose. Some graphs are better suited than others to display certain types of data.

Frequency tables use numbers or tally marks to record data. Tally marks are useful while collecting initial data. Usually the data in a frequency table will be displayed visually in a line plot or graph.

Line plots begin with a number line containing numbers that include the entire range of the data. Then one X is placed above a number each time it occurs in the data. As in bar graphs, the heights of the columns above each number provide a quick, visual way to compare data. Line plots are useful for small sets of data in which the frequencies are less than 10.

Bar graphs show discrete, or separate, data about a small number of categories. Heights of buildings, speeds of cars, and costs of various items are all appropriate classes of data to be represented by a bar graph.

A bar graph, like a line graph and coordinate grid, displays data on an *x*-axis and a *y*-axis. Explain that the *x*-axis is the horizontal line at the bottom of the graph. Typically, the *x*-axis lists the categories. The *y*-axis shows the scale, or the numbers chosen to represent the data. Point out that many scales use multiples of 2, 4, 5, 10, and 100. Finding the number halfway between the lines on a scale can help students reasonably estimate the values of bars that fall between the lines of the graph.

Like a line plot, the height (or length if presented horizontally) of the bars makes visual comparisons easy. For a bar graph to be "fair," all bars on the same graph should be of equal width.

Line graphs are best suited to displaying continuous data, usually data that changes over time, such as temperatures. The points can be thought of as snapshots that show exactly what happened at a specific point within the continuum. Drawing the lines to connect the points makes it easy to interpret data that happened between one point and the next. To be "fair," all sections of the grid on which a line graph is drawn should be the same size and should represent the same quantity. Line graphs can show trends, such as increases and decreases in sales.

Coordinate grids use ordered pairs to plot discrete points that show a relationship between two numerical scales. Remind students that in an ordered pair, the first number tells them how far to move along the *x*-axis, and the second number tells them how far to move along the *y*-axis.

Circle graphs are used to compare parts to a whole. The circle represents one whole, and the sections represent the parts. Each section is proportional to the part of the whole that it represents.

Lesson 2.8

MEASURES OF CENTRAL TENDENCY To determine a measure of central tendency, students must find the one number that best describes the middle of the data. The most useful form of this "average" may be the *mean*, *median*, *mode*, or *range*, depending on the data. The *mean* equalizes the value of each piece of data. Extremely high or low numbers that differ vastly from the rest of the data will skew the mean and make it inappropriate as an average. The *median* is helpful as an average if in addition to being the middle numeral, it is also in the middle of the range of numbers. The *mode* is least often used because it is usually unrepresentative of the entire data set. However, for non-numeric data, such as the favorite colors of your students, it may be the only option available.

CHAPTER 2

Tips for New Teachers
Use with Chapter 2.

Lesson 2.1

TEACHING TIP Have students suggest objects in the room that have a length or height of about 1 foot. Then have students use a ruler to verify their suggestions. Label the length of each accepted object. Repeat this activity with measures of about 1 yard and about 1 meter. Have students use these visual benchmarks to estimate the lengths of other objects in the room.

INCLUSION Have students interview their parents or other adults about any uncommon units of length they have used either in their work or in another part of the world. List these units on a chart and post it in the classroom. (See the example below.) Keep adding to the list as the chapter progresses. Students will be impressed at the variety of units that people use.

Unit of Length	How long in customary units?	Where or for what is this unit used?
li	About $\frac{1}{2}$ mile	China
mil	$\frac{1}{1000}$ inch	Thickness of plastic sheets
pica	$\frac{1}{6}$ inch	Printing

Lesson 2.2

COMMON ERROR Ask students which price for carpeting is more expensive: $10 per square foot or $40 per square yard. Because students have seen the conversion factor 1 yard = 3 feet so often, many will not understand why $40 per square yard is cheaper. Have students draw a square grid that is 3 feet on each side to illustrate that 1 square yard = 9 square feet. They can then compare the prices per square yard: $90 per square yard versus $40 per square yard.

INCLUSION This may be a first experience with formulas for some students. Explain to these students that a formula is a "recipe" for solving a particular type of problem, such as an area or perimeter problem. Emphasize that to use formulas successfully, students must remember what measure each variable represents, such as ℓ for length and w for width. Usually the letter of the variable is a good clue.

Lesson 2.3

INCLUSION Order and relationship are essential when comparing units of measure within problems relating to scale. Many students fail to organize their work, and they confuse related measures.

For Example 3 on page 69, suggest that students use a 2 by 2 table. The labels for the columns and rows show the types of measurements being compared and where the lengths are found.

	Model Length	Actual Length
From the Scale	1 in.	2 ft
From the Actual Boat	?	18 ft

The lengths of the model are proportional to the lengths of the actual boat. The actual boat length of 18 feet is 9 times 2 feet (given as part of the scale). This means that the length of the model is also 9 times the 1 inch given as the other part of the scale. Therefore, the length of the model boat is 9 inches.

Lesson 2.4

TEACHING TIP Have students draw their line plots on graph paper, using one square for each X. This will make the height of each column of Xs proportional to its tally and give a clearer picture of the data. The line plot then becomes, in effect, a histogram.

Hands-on Activity 2.5

TEACHING TIP Consider having students collect data about themselves and their fellow students. Some suggestions for topics are the number of pets they own, the month in which they were born, or the number of books inside their backpack. Avoid topics that may be sensitive in nature.

Tips for New Teachers

Use with Chapter 2.

Lesson 2.5

INCLUSION For Example 1 on page 79, help students who have trouble locating a height of 43 for the bar. Have them imagine that the region between 40 and 50 has 9 equally spaced lines between them. The bar for 43 then ends at the third (imaginary) line above the line for 40.

TEACHING TIP For Example 2, draw students' attention to the color coding in the graph. Ask students about any other color-coded graphs they have seen before. Tell them that color coding is an effective way to graph complex sets of related data without cluttering up the visual display. For example, by adding a third color, the data for an eighth-grade class could be added to the graph in Example 2 without adding any new words to the display.

Lesson 2.6

INCLUSION For students who confuse the terms *vertical* and *horizontal*, draw a picture of a sun rising on the horizon and connect the word horizontal to the word horizon.

TEACHING TIP Have students note that coordinate grids have the same intervals on the horizontal and vertical scales. In line graphs, the intervals on the horizontal scale may be different from those on the vertical scale. The intervals on each axis of a line graph should be chosen independently to fit the range of the data being represented.

Lesson 2.7

TEACHING TIP Example 2 on page 89 is actually a probability problem. By assuming that the survey of 100 students is representative of the 300 student guests at the party, you can predict what the guests will choose: they will choose vanilla at about the same rate as the sample of 100 students. Since the number of guests is 3 times the number of students in the survey, about three times as many guests will choose vanilla.

COMMON ERROR Students tend to think that any data that can be displayed in a bar graph can also be displayed in a circle graph. Be sure that students understand that the data for a circle graph must represent a whole. Use the descriptions of the following data sets to explain the difference between the two types of graphs.

— a survey of pet owners about the type and number of pets they have

— data showing the number of travelers through three of the busiest airports

In the first example, some people may have cats, dogs, and fish, which would put a tally in three categories for one person. The total would represent more than the whole list of people. In the second example, since the data is for only three of many airports, many travelers would not be represented in this data. The number of travelers in the data would be less than the whole set of travelers. This means that neither data set would be appropriate for circle graphs.

Hands-on Activity 2.8

INCLUSION For kinesthetic learners, the "equaling out" of the stacks of counters is an important link in their understanding of the concept of the mean. Encourage all students to stack counters so that they can develop a concrete understanding of the mean.

Lesson 2.8

TEACHING TIP Students usually think of the "average" of a set of data as the mean. They then wonder why they need the two other averages: the mode and the median. Show them these data sets to help them understand.

— favorite color of six students: blue, red, red, yellow, red, black

— selling price of homes in one week: $165,000, $170,000, $165,000, $2,000,000

In the first example, no mean or median exists. The mode is the only average that can be used to describe what color the students typically choose.

In the second example, the mean of the prices is $625,000, which does not describe the data well—no item is even close to that price. However, a median of $167,500 is fairly descriptive of most of the data. Data in which one number is much greater or much less than the others, such as home sales data, is best described using a median.

Chapter 2

Name _____ **Date** _____

Parents as Partners
Use with Chapter 2.

Chapter Overview One way you can help your student succeed in Chapter 2 is by discussing the lesson goals in the chart below. When a lesson is completed, ask your student the following questions. "What were the goals of the lesson? What new words and formulas did you learn? How can you apply the ideas of the lesson to your life?"

Lesson Title	Lesson Goals	Key Applications
2.1: Measuring Length	Measure length using customary and metric units. Choose appropriate units. Estimate length using benchmarks.	• Animal Length • Door Height • Rock Climbing
2.2: Perimeter and Area	Use formulas to find perimeter and area. Solve for an unknown dimension.	• Carnival Size • Fencing • Home Improvement • Gymnastics
2.3: Scale Drawings	Use scale drawings to find actual lengths.	• Model Boat • Maps • Lighthouses
2.4: Frequency Tables and Line Plots	Create and interpret frequency tables and line plots.	• Summer Reading • Volunteer Fire Department • Weather
2.5: Bar Graphs	Display data using bar graphs and double bar graphs.	• Environmental Protection • Mountain Ranges • International Movie Prices
2.6: Coordinates and Line Graphs	Plot points on coordinate grids and make line graphs.	• Radio Stations • Endangered Birds • Internet
2.7: Circle Graphs	Interpret circle graphs and make predictions.	• Ice Cream • Population • Oceans • Marine Mammals
2.8: Mean, Median, and Mode	Describe data using mean, median, mode, and range.	• Astronauts • Scores • Sea Turtles

Know How to Take Notes

Taking Notes While Reading is the strategy featured in Chapter 2 (see page 54). Encourage your student to leave extra space while taking notes in class. Have your student read and explain his/her class notes to you. If your student is unclear about something, discuss what information could be added to the notes to make them more understandable and useable as a study tool. Compare your student's comprehension of notes written in his/her own words, to that of notes copied word for word.

Chapter 2 Continued

Parents as Partners
Use with Chapter 2.

Key Ideas Your student can demonstrate understanding of key concepts by working through the following exercises with you.

Lesson	Exercise
2.1	Estimate the length of your waist in inches and centimeters, then measure to check your estimate. (Hint: Use a string to go around your waist, then measure the length of the string.)
2.2	The perimeter of the square poster in your room is 60 inches. What is the length of each side? What is the area? Challenge: If a poster with the same perimeter is a rectangle with a width of 12 inches, what is its length? What is its area?
2.3	The scale for a model car is 2 cm : 16 cm. Find the length of each part. a. the actual wheel, if the model's wheel is 8 centimeters b. the model's seat, if the actual seat is 152 centimeters
2.4	Record the number of cars, trucks, SUVs, vans, and "other" vehicles that pass by your home (or a nearby intersection if your street isn't that busy) during a 30 minute period. Make a frequency table and line plot to display your data.
2.5	Use your data from the Lesson 2.4 question to create a bar graph.
2.6	Explain why a line graph is not a suitable way to show your data from the Lesson 2.4 question.
2.7	Use your data from the Lesson 2.4 question to create a circle graph.
2.8	Use the game scores to find the mean, median, and mode(s) of the points scored per game by the home football team. Home: 21 7 14 0 0 14 34 27 0 Opponent: 7 15 13 49 46 34 15 34 29

Home Involvement Activity

Directions: Make a scale drawing of your room using the scale 1 in. : 2 ft. Include at least 4 items that are in your room (for example: bed, dresser, area rug, stereo). Be sure to include any doors, windows or closets you have as well.

Answers

2.1: Answers will vary. (Range in inches should be between 15–40, centimeters between 38–102.) **2.2:** Square poster: length: 15 in., area: 225 in.²; Rectangular poster: length 18 in., area: 216 in.² **2.3: a.** 64 cm **b.** 19 cm **2.4–2.5:** Answers will vary. **2.6:** A line graph is used to show a change over time. The data collected do not reflect this. **2.7:** Answers will vary. **2.8:** Mean: 13, Median: 14, Mode: 0

CHAPTER 2

Bulletin Board Idea

Use with Chapter 2.

Objective

To visually reinforce the concepts of collecting, organizing, and graphing data.

Materials

- 2 sheets of construction paper
- 3 sheets of graph paper
- 3 sentence strips

Constructing the Bulletin Board

1. Using construction paper, create a table entitled "Favorite Sports Among Students" that shows that 43 students prefer to play baseball, 33 prefer to play football, 59 prefer to play soccer, and 38 prefer to play basketball.

2. On the graph paper, display the data using three types of graphs: bar graph, circle graph, and line graph. Label each graph with a key and post the graphs on the board.

3. On three sentence strips, write the following questions:
   - Which sport was chosen most often by students? Chosen least often?
   - Which graph do you think is easiest to read for this set of data?
   - Can you think of a type of data that would be best represented on a line graph?

Using the Bulletin Board

After students complete Lesson 2.7, discuss the bulletin board and its questions. Explain that data can be represented in many ways, and sometimes one type of graph may be better than another for a particular data set. The discussion and the solution to the problem posed on the bulletin board may include the following points.

- Collecting data accurately and finding the best way to display it are important for making a valid interpretation of the data. If the data is not accurate, or the graph of it is misleading, the interpretation may be incorrect.

- Whether data is best displayed in a table, bar graph, line graph, or circle graph depends on the type of data. A bar graph is best for comparing categories of data. A line graph is often used to show change. A circle graph is used to show how the data is broken down into parts of a whole.

- How the graph is read depends on the type of graph. The greatest value in a bar graph is the tallest bar; in a line graph, the greatest value is the highest point; and in a circle graph, the greatest value is the largest wedge.

Follow-up

- Have students bring to class graphs and tables that display data in magazines and newspapers. Discuss with the class whether the data display is easy to understand and not misleading. Give students the opportunity to interpret the data.

CHAPTER 3

Math Behind the Math
Use with Chapter 3.

Lesson 3.1

DECIMAL PLACE VALUE The word *decimal* is derived from the Latin word *decima*, which means *a tenth part*. Each place in a number has a value 10 times the place to its right. The numbers 7, 70, and 700 show how the value of the 7 within each number depends on where the 7 and the 0 are placed.

Number systems different greatly from culture to culture. In our number system, the digits 0–9 signify their value by the place, or position, they occupy in the number. The numbers 990, 90, and 9.09 all contain the digits 9 and 0, but the position of the digits indicates their value. This is why our system is called the decimal place-value system. Without it, many more digits than 0–9 would be needed to represent all possible numbers.

The origins of the decimal place-value system lie within the *Hindu-Arabic* system because mathematicians from India established it more than 2000 years ago. During the ninth and tenth centuries, Arab astronomers and mathematicians, such as al-Khawarizmi, popularized this system throughout the Middle East, Spain, and North Africa.

When studying whole-number place value, students learned that in the base-ten system, each place claims a value ten times greater than the place to its right. This concept also applies when students consider the numbers that are less than one. Placing a decimal point to the right of the ones place separates whole numbers from decimals less than one.

4	0	0	0.			
	4	0	0.			
		4	0.			
			4.			
			0.	4		
			0.	0	4	
			0.	0	0	4

Since students are less familiar with decimal numbers than whole numbers, consider reviewing decimal place value using dollars, dimes, and pennies. Ask students to write in a place-value chart the value of 1 dollar as 1.0, 70 pennies as 0.70, and 7 pennies as 0.07. You can point out that 70 hundredths (or 70 pennies) equals 7 tenths (or 7 dimes).

A source of confusion for some students is recognizing the equal value of numbers such as 0.4, 0.40, 0.400, and 0.4000. Exploring this equivalence concept will help students when they annex zeros, in order to compare, order, add, subtract, multiply, and divide decimals.

Lesson 3.2

DECIMALS AND METRICS Because the metric system was designed as a base-ten system, its structure and organization is similar to the place-value system.

Place Value	Metric Units	
Thousands	Kilometer	× 10
Hundreds	Hectometer	× 10
Tens	Dekameter	× 10
Ones	Meter	× 10
Tenths	Decimeter	× 10
Hundredths	Centimeter	× 10
Thousandths	Millimeter	× 10

When the metric system was designed, Greek prefixes were assigned to the places to the left of the decimal point to represent whole units. Latin prefixes were assigned to the decimal places to the right of the decimal point to represent fractions of units.

- In the metric system, the basic unit of length is the *meter*.
- Dividing 1 meter into tenths creates 10 decimeters. Each *decimeter* is one tenth of a meter.
- Dividing 1 decimeter into tenths creates 10 centimeters. Each *centimeter* is one hundredth of a meter.
- Dividing 1 centimeter into tenths creates 1 millimeter. Each *millimeter* is one thousandth of a meter.

Middle School Math, Course 1
Professional Development Book

CHAPTER 3 Continued

Math Behind the Math

Use with Chapter 3.

A person's purpose for measuring determines the level of precision needed to describe a measure. Generally, the lesser units are more precise measures. The measurement 1.52 meters can be interpreted as:

about 1 and a half meters, or

1 meter and about 5 decimeters, or

1 meter and 52 centimeters, or

1520 millimeters.

Lesson 3.3

ORDERING DECIMALS Just as there are an infinite number of decimal places in the decimal place-value system, there are an infinite number of decimal numbers between any two whole numbers or two decimal numbers. On a number line, the space between two numbers can be continually subdivided by tens into more and more decimal places.

When comparing and ordering numbers, aligning the decimal points assures that the numbers to be compared have the same place value. Begin with the leading digit and compare ones to ones, tenths to tenths, hundredths to hundredths, and so on. Writing zeros to the right of a decimal will not change its value, but it may help some students compare the decimals.

Lessons 3.4–3.5

DECIMAL ROUNDING AND ESTIMATION Often when rounding a number, you are essentially looking for a number that is easy to compute mentally. You want to know which ten (or hundred or thousand) the number is closest to. If you picture or draw a number line, it is easy to see why digits that are 5 or greater are rounded up and digits less than 5 are rounded down. These whole-number rounding rules also apply to decimals less than one. Depending on the level of precision needed, decimals can be rounded to the nearest one, tenth, hundredth, thousandth, and so on. For many purposes, rounding decimals to the nearest whole number will provide a reasonable estimate of the answer. Rounding to the nearest whole number also makes computation easier.

When you round large numbers, you can write them in standard form, or you can use a short, written form that incorporates decimals. By established convention, a number in the millions rounded to the ten thousands or hundred thousands place is often written in short word form. This convention also applies to the billions.

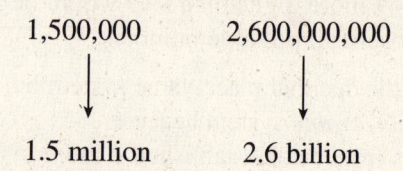

$$1{,}500{,}000 \qquad 2{,}600{,}000{,}000$$
$$\downarrow \qquad\qquad \downarrow$$
$$1.5 \text{ million} \qquad 2.6 \text{ billion}$$

Lesson 3.6

ADDING AND SUBTRACTING DECIMALS When using base-ten models to add and subtract decimals, students need to keep in mind that a hundreds square represents one, a tens rod represents one tenth, and a single square represents one hundredth.

When adding and subtracting decimals, it is important to add numbers that have the same place value. Aligning the decimal points helps assure that tenths will be added to tenths, and so on. Other than aligning the decimal and whole-number places and writing the decimal point in the answer, the process of adding and subtracting decimals is the same as adding and subtracting whole numbers. This is because decimals, like whole numbers, can be regrouped or renamed across place values.

Chapter 3: Tips for New Teachers
Use with Chapter 3.

Lesson 3.1
TEACHING TIP Although it is common to read the number 1.16 as "one point sixteen" outside the classroom, ask students to avoid this usage in the classroom. It de-emphasizes place-value concepts and does not mirror the language used on tests. Instead, encourage students to read 1.16 as "one **and** sixteen hundredths."

TEACHING TIP For Example 1a on page 107, have students write the numbers 20 hundredths and 2 tenths as decimals. Help them notice that 0.20 and 0.2 represent the same number of base-ten pieces. Remind students that zeros may be written to the right of the digits in a decimal number without changing its value. This is because zeros to the right of a decimal do not change the value of the digits in other places.

Hands-on Activity 3.2
INCLUSION Some students may need extra help using rulers. It may be helpful to project a clear centimeter/millimeter ruler on the overhead projector. Have students practice locating numbers on the centimeter scale and reading the scale as you point to different marks. Also, when students are measuring, be sure they start each measurement at the endpoint of the centimeter scale, which is often not the end of the ruler.

Lesson 3.2
INCLUSION If students confuse centimeters and millimeters, have them think of other words that stem from the Latin prefixes *centi-* and *milli-*, such as *century* and *millennium*. Tell them that a "century" is a "span of 100 years" and that a "millennium" is a "span of 1000 years." There are ten centuries within a millennium.

This connection will help students recognize that *centi-* means *hundredths* and *milli-* means *thousandths*. Note that *milli-* and *kilo-* both mean *thousand*. The prefixes for units shorter than one meter are from the Latin language and prefixes for units longer than one meter are from the Greek language.

INCLUSION For kinesthetic learners, have students identify distances in the classroom that would most reasonably be measured in meters (length of the classroom), centimeters (width of a textbook), and millimeters (thickness of the cover of a textbook). Have them measure each distance and tell why the unit they suggested is appropriate.

Lesson 3.3
INCLUSION For students who confuse the symbols < and >, remind them that the smaller end of the arrow is next to the smaller number.

COMMON ERROR Some students think that a decimal number with fewer digits is less than a decimal number with more digits. For example, students may assume that 2.9 is less than 2.79. Remind them that unlike whole numbers, the number of digits does not help to compare decimals. Before students begin comparing two decimals, they should write them with the same number of digits. Then they can compare the decimal parts just as they do whole numbers. When they compare the decimal part of 2.90 and 2.79, they can see that 2.79 is the lesser number.

Lesson 3.4
TEACHING TIP To help students who are challenged by rounding, ask that they break down the steps using the following process.

Round 5.134 to the nearest tenth.

Step 1	Underscore the place you are rounding to.
5.1̲34	
Step 2	Circle the number to the right.
5.1③4	
Step 3	Round, using the rules for rounding.
5.1	

Remind students that in real life, the context determines which digit they round a number to. Usually, it is to a place that allows the rounded number to be mentally added to or subtracted from others.

CHAPTER 3 Continued
Tips for New Teachers
Use with Chapter 3.

TEACHING TIP Have students find graphs in newspapers or on the Internet that show large numbers, such as in Example 4 on page 126. When students see how often large numbers are expressed as decimals, they will become more comfortable with this form of writing numbers.

Lesson 3.5

TEACHING TIP Discuss with students how they might use high and low estimates. They should understand that when they are estimating costs, such as the cost of items for a camping trip, they should use a high estimate. When they are estimating earnings, such as the amount of money the Jazz Band will earn from a concert, they should use a low estimate. These estimation methods will insure they not run out of money.

TEACHING TIP When adjusting a front-end estimate, some students may not know what to do with the extra amounts that do not total 1. For example, consider the following sum.

```
   3.09
   4.31  ⎤
   1.77  ⎦ about 1
 + 6.43
   ────
   14
```

Then .09 and .43 have not been accounted for. There are three options here.

1. Round both decimals to 0 to get an estimate of 15.

2. Add the two decimals mentally to get 0.52, which rounds to 1. The total estimate is 16.

3. Add the two decimals mentally, and round to 0.5. The total estimate is then 15.5.

Students should recognize that all three estimates are appropriate and the one you choose in real life is the one that best suits the purpose. The first estimate is low, the second estimate is high, and the third is a very close estimate.

Lesson 3.6

INCLUSION To help students who confuse the names of the associative and commutative properties, remind them that an *association* is a group of people. Similarly, the associative property is the grouping property—it explains how to group three numbers so that they can be added. A *commuter* is one who travels, or moves, to work. Similarly, the commutative property explains how to move numbers in an expression.

TEACHING TIP Have students estimate the answers to decimal addition and subtraction problems before working them out. Then the estimate can be used to check that the sum or difference is reasonable. Students can use this self-checking device to increase the number of accurate answers.

46 Middle School Math, Course 1
Professional Development Book

CHAPTER 3

Name _____ Date _____

Parents as Partners

Use with Chapter 3.

Chapter Overview One way you can help your student succeed in Chapter 3 is by discussing the lesson goals in the chart below. When a lesson is completed, ask your student the following questions. "What were the goals of the lesson? What new words and formulas did you learn? How can you apply the ideas of the lesson to your life?"

Lesson Title	Lesson Goals	Key Applications
3.1: Decimals and Place Value	Read and write decimals.	• Swimming • Auto Racing • Turbojets • Bridges • Gemstones
3.2: Measuring Metric Lengths	Use decimals to express metric measurements.	• Dinosaurs • Pancakes • Sea Otters
3.3: Ordering Decimals	Compare and order decimals.	• Mongolian Gerbil • Telephone Calls • Milk Prices • Volcanoes
3.4: Rounding Decimals	Round decimals. Use decimals for large numbers.	• Miniature Guitar • Baseball Salaries • Skateboarding • Hair Width
3.5: Decimal Estimation	Estimate sums and differences of decimals. Predict the change from a shopping purchase.	• Sports Participants • Shopping • Groceries • Mountains
3.6: Adding and Subtracting Decimals	Add and subtract decimals. Evaluate algebraic expressions. Write a verbal model.	• Bakery • Banking • Orienteering • Astronauts

Know How to Take Notes

Homework is the strategy featured in Chapter 3 (see page 106.) Encourage your student to write down any questions he/she may have in a notebook while doing homework. Have your student record the teacher's answer to the question as well. Once your student has received the teacher's answer, ask your student to explain the answer so you can check his/her understanding.

Middle School Math, Course 1
Professional Development Book

CHAPTER 3 Continued

Name _____ Date _____

Parents as Partners

Use with Chapter 3.

Key Ideas Your student can demonstrate understanding of key concepts by working through the following exercises with you.

Lesson	Exercise
3.1	The scores three gymnasts received in the floor competition are given below in words. Write the scores as decimals. Which gymnast won? Gymnast A: seven and eighty-four hundredths Gymnast B: seven and ninety-three thousandths Gymnast C: seven and six hundred five thousandths
3.2	Write each measurement in the specified decimal form. (a) A shirt sleeve is forty-seven centimeters long (hundredth of a meter). (b) A new kitten's tail is twenty-nine centimeters long (hundredth of a meter). (c) Your eraser is five and two tenths centimeters long (tenth of a centimeter).
3.3	Complete the statement with <, >, or = . (a) 4.14 _?_ 4.1 (b) 2.051 _?_ 2.009 (c) 7.89 _?_ 7.93 (d) 25.6 _?_ 25.60
3.4	Round the decimal as specified. (a) 5.079 (nearest tenth) (b) 8.2124 (nearest thousandth) (c) 4.3737 (nearest hundredth) (d) 0.00681 (leading digit) (e) 5,394,200 (nearest hundred thousand, then write as a decimal number of millions).
3.5	Estimate the sum or difference. (a) 10.68 + 9.73 (b) 11.250 − 6.81 (c) 5.99 − 3.04 (d) 8.21 + 13.38 + 4.51
3.6	Evaluate the expression when $x = 3.9$ and $y = 7.04$. (a) $x + 8.1$ (b) $10.72 - y$ (c) $y - x$ (d) $x - 1.75$ (e) $5.29 + x$ (f) $y + 0.34$

Home Involvement Activity

Directions: Select five common grocery items, e.g. bread, milk, eggs, cereal, juice. Estimate whether $10 is enough to buy the items. Is $20? Go to a grocery store and find the prices. Use front-end estimation to approximate the total cost. Then find the actual cost and see how good your estimates were.

Answers

3.1: Gymnast A: 7.84; Gymnast B: 7.093; Gymnast C: 7.605; Gymnast A won. **3.2:** (a) 0.47 (b) 0.29 (c) 5.2 **3.3:** (a) > (b) > (c) < (d) = **3.4:** (a) 5.1 (b) 8.212 (c) 4.37 (d) 0.007 (e) 5,400,000; 5.4 million **3.5:** (a) 21 (b) 4 (c) 3 (d) 26 **3.6:** (a) 12 (b) 3.68 (c) 3.14 (d) 2.15 (e) 9.19 (f) 7.38

48 Middle School Math, Course 1
Professional Development Book

Chapter 3

Bulletin Board Idea

Use with Chapter 3.

Objective

To use the context and data from the Unit 1 poster to compare and order decimals and to add and subtract decimals.

Materials

- 3 sentence strips
- 4 stickie notes (3 in. by 3 in.)
- colored tape
- Unit 1 poster: Winning with Decimals
- 4 colored pushpins (red, blue, green, yellow)

Constructing the Bulletin Board

1. On the first sentence strip, write the title of the bulletin board, "Decimal Field Days." The second and third sentence strips, write "In what order did the teams complete Lap 3?" and "Finish Line."

2. On the four stickie notes write the names of the four teams (Red, Blue, Green, Yellow), leaving room for students to write the total time for three laps.

3. Position the title strip at the top of the bulletin board and the Unit 1 poster to the left, below the title. Place the second strip to the right of the poster. Beneath this strip, use colored tape to indicate the length of the track. Use the "Finish Line" sentence strip to indicate the finish line. Using colored pushpins, attach the four sticky notes below the track.

Using the Bulletin Board

After students have completed Lesson 3.6, discuss the bulletin board and its question with the class. The discussion may include the following.

- Ask students how they can tell which team was in first place at the end of Lap 3. Students should suggest adding the times for the three laps and ordering the sums. Be sure they recognize that the winner is the team with the least time.

- Have students write the sum of the times for the three laps for each team on the four sticky notes. Then have them position the sticky notes near the finish line in the order in which the teams will cross the line.

- Read the question on the poster. Ask how much faster than the first-place team must each of the other teams run in Lap 4 in order to win. Students should see that they can subtract the total time for the second-, third-, and fourth-place teams from the time for the first-place team.

Follow-up

- When students have completed the worksheet on the back of the poster, ask them to write algebraic sentences that express the relationships among the data.

CHAPTER 4

Math Behind the Math

Use with Chapter 4.

Lesson 4.1

ESTIMATING DECIMAL PRODUCTS When multiplying with decimal factors, it is important to estimate the product before multiplying. Estimating first helps students know where to place the decimal point in the product. If the factors are decimals greater than one, then rounding to the nearest whole number provides a reasonable estimate of the product. When multiplying 2.75 × 5, an appropriate estimate is 3 × 5, or 15. Therefore, the answer cannot be 1.5, 0.15, or 1500. Likewise, rounding factors that are decimals less than one to 0, 0.5, or 1 helps students recognize that 3 × 0.004 will be close to 3 × 0, or 0. The product of 3 × 0.004 cannot reasonably be 12 or 1.2.

More than 2000 years ago, both the Mayan and the Hindu cultures used the concept of zero within their number systems. With the introduction of the zero as a placeholder, each numeral has a value based on its position within the number. Thinking about an expression such as 7 × 0.006 as 7 times 6 thousandths helps students recognize that their product must be 42 thousandths, or 0.042.

Encourage students to practice the procedural method for placing the decimal point in the product. Have them find the sum of the decimal places in the factors, and then, within the product, have them count that number of places from right to left in order to position the decimal point. At the same time, look for opportunities to improve their understanding of a placeholder zero, which will help them to develop their number sense.

Lesson 4.2

THE DISTRIBUTIVE PROPERTY The distributive property allows you to distribute or arrange factors within a multiplication expression. After doing this, multiplication becomes an easier task. For example, 7 × 35 is a simpler to compute if you think of it as (7 × 30) + (7 × 5).

Students may not have recognized the distributive property as they multiplied whole numbers, but when they wrote each partial product, they were in essence distributing the factors.

6 × 78 = (6 × 8) + (6 × 70)

```
   78
 ×  6
   48     6 × 8 ones = 48
   42     6 × 7 tens = 42 tens
  468
```

Multiplying and recording the partial products in the multiplication algorithm is just one way students use the distributive property.

Lesson 4.3

NUMBER SENSE AND MULTIPLYING DECIMALS When students multiply whole numbers, their expectation is that the product will be equal to or greater than either factor. When multiplying two factors that are decimals less than one, this expectation is turned upside down. This is because when multiplying decimals less than one, students are finding part of a part, which is less than either part. The product then must be less than either factor. Think of the simplest decimal multiplication: 0.1 × 0.1 = 0.01. The first model below shows 1 tenth. The next model shows 1 tenth of 1 tenth, or 1 hundredth.

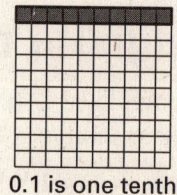

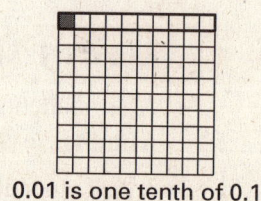

0.1 is one tenth   0.01 is one tenth of 0.1

Lessons 4.4

ESTIMATING DECIMAL QUOTIENTS The process for dividing with decimals is the same as dividing with whole numbers. The most challenging part of dividing with decimals is writing the first digit in the quotient properly. Emphasize the discipline of first writing the quotient's decimal point above the decimal point in the dividend.

For problems such as 32.4 ÷ 6, ask students to round the dividend and then estimate. Have them drop the decimal number and think 32 ÷ 6. Next, have them write compatible numbers to help them decide where to write the first number in the

Math Behind the Math

Use with Chapter 4.

quotient. For example, 30 ÷ 6 = 5. The first number in the quotient will be written in the ones place.

When the dividend is less than the divisor, ask students to actually write out their estimates before placing the first digit in the quotient. For example, in the problem 8.0 ÷ 20, students should write out their estimates: 20 × 4 = 80; 20 × 0.4 = 8.0. Paying careful attention to the difference between 4 and 0.4 will help students properly place the first digit in the quotient.

Writing zeros to the right of a decimal number does not change its value, but it does allow division to continue beyond the place shown in the dividend. Some division problems result in a quotient that is finite or terminating: 10 ÷ 8 = 1.25. Others division problems result in a quotient that continues indefinitely: 1 ÷ 3 = 0.33333.... Drawing a bar over the repeating part of the decimal quotient is a shorthand way of indicating this.

$$0.333333\ldots = 0.\overline{3} \qquad 0.090909\ldots = \overline{09}$$

Lesson 4.5–4.6

PLACE VALUE AND POWERS OF TEN In the base-ten place-value system, when you multiply by ten or a power of ten (such as 100, 1000, 10,000 or 0.1, 0.01, 0.001), you are shifting the value of the other factor within the place value chart. The decimal point of the other factor moves to the right when multiplied by 10, 100 or 1000. The decimal point of the other factor moves to the left when multiplied by 0.1, 0.01, or 0.001. This pattern of decimal-point movement helps you to multiply mentally.

Have students make a card that illustrates these patterns. Ask them to tape the card to their desk for easy reference.

Multiplying by Whole-Number Powers of Ten

4 × 10 = 40.   4 × 100 = 400.
4 × 1000 = 4000.

Multiplying by Decimal Powers of Ten

4 × 0.1 = 0.4   4 × 0.01 = 0.04
4 × 0.001 = 0.004

Dividing by Whole-Number Powers of Ten

4 ÷ 10 = 0.4   4 ÷ 100 = 0.04
4 ÷ 1000 = 0.004

Dividing by Decimal Powers of Ten

4 ÷ 0.1 = 40.   4 ÷ 0.01 = 400.
4 ÷ 0.001 = 4000.

Lesson 4.7–4.8

EXTENDING THE METRIC SYSTEM The prefixes students learned for the metric units of length are the same prefixes used for metric units of mass and capacity. Mass is the amount of matter that makes up any object. In the metric system, the base unit of mass is the gram, and the base unit of volume, or capacity, is the liter. A liter is the volume of a cubic decimeter. A kiloliter is the volume of a cubic meter. Liters are abbreviated with a capital L so as not to confuse it with the lower case ℓ (used for length) or the number 1.

The customary system uses units of weight. Weight on Earth is the force that Earth's gravity exerts on the mass of an object. That is why objects in space have considerably less weight than they do on Earth, even though they have the same mass.

Regardless of the system of measurement, you divide to change from a smaller to a larger unit. This is because there will be fewer larger units than there were smaller units.

1000 g = 1 kg

Divide by 1000 to change grams to kilograms:
5356 g = 5.356 kg because
5356 ÷ 1000 = 5.356.

Conversely, you multiply to change from a larger unit to a smaller unit. There will be a greater number of smaller units than there were larger units.

1 L = 1000 mL

Multiply by 1000 to change liters to milliliters: 2 L = 2000 mL because
2 × 1000 = 2000.

Chapter 4: Tips for New Teachers

Use with Chapter 4.

Lesson 4.1

TEACHING TIP After working through Example 2 on page 154, have students multiply by 10 the decimals in Examples 1 and 2 using the technique shown in Example 2. Ask students to describe the shortcut method for multiplying by 10, which is to move the decimal one place to the right. This is good preparatory work for Lesson 4.5, in which students will find shortcuts for multiplying by all powers of 10.

TEACHING TIP For Example 3 on page 154, have students determine whether the estimate is high or low. Students should see that since 8.875 is rounded up and 18 is not rounded, the estimate will be a high estimate.

Lesson 4.2

TEACHING TIP Students may be surprised to find that the multiplication algorithm for 2-digit numbers is based on the distributive property. Use this example to help them see this connection.

24×56 can be written as $(20 + 4)(50 + 6)$

```
  50 + 6  can be shortened to      56
× 20 + 4                         ×  24
─────────                        ─────
 4 × 6  =   24  ─┐
 4 × 50 =  200  ─┴──────────     224
20 × 6  =  120  ─┐
20 × 50 = 1000  ─┴──────────    1120
         ─────                  ─────
          1344                   1344
```

TEACHING TIP This is a good time to have students begin a formulas page in their notebooks. Remind them that they worked with formulas for perimeter and area in Lesson 2.2. Those formulas should be included in their notebooks, along with the distance formula. For each formula, have students write its name, its symbolic form, and a list of what each variable represents. Then have students write at least one worked out example for each formula.

Have students add other formulas to their notebook as the year progresses.

Lesson 4.3

TEACHING TIP For many multiplication problems, an estimate can help guide students in placing the decimal point.

Problem	Estimate	Answer
$5.4 \times 4.1 \stackrel{?}{=} 2214$ → $5 \times 4 = 20$		22.14
$0.9 \times 2.7 \stackrel{?}{=} 243$ → $1 \times 3 = 3.0$		2.43

Because of this, students may wonder why they need to learn a rule for placing the decimal point in a product when they can simply estimate. Remind students that although an estimate works well for most products, some products, such as 0.012×0.00638, are more difficult to estimate. In this case, using the rule for placing the decimal point is essential.

TEACHING TIP For Example 1 on page 164, have students explain why when they multiply 0.2×0.6, the product 0.12 is reasonable. Many may notice that the factor 0.6 is less than 1. When they multiply 0.2 by a number less than 1, the product is less than 0.2.

Lesson 4.4

TEACHING TIP Suggest that students estimate quotients before they compute. Then have them compare their computed answer to their estimated answer. This method develops students' number sense and allows them to check their answers for reasonableness. For Example 1 on page 169, ask students how much a set of 8 cards would cost if each card costs $1. ($8) Next, ask students how much a set of cards would cost if each card costs $2. ($16) From this, students should see that the quotient must be between $1 and $2.

COMMON ERROR In Example 3 on page 170, the problem is $7 \div 23$. Watch for students who transpose the numbers and divide 23 by 7. Many students are in the habit of dividing the greater number by the lesser number. To help these students, review the terms *dividend*, *divisor*, and *quotient*, and their position in a number sentence and in the algorithmic display.

Chapter 4 Continued

Tips for New Teachers
Use with Chapter 4.

Lesson 4.5

INCLUSION For students who get confused about the direction in which to move a decimal point when multiplying or dividing by powers of ten, have them make a chart with examples for quick and easy reference.

TEACHING TIP Have students copy the following chart in their notebook. Ask pairs of students to look for patterns within the chart that might help them remember the structure and organization for writing all powers of ten.

Powers of Ten	
$10 \times 10 \times 10$	$1000. = 10^3$
10×10	$100. = 10^2$
10	$10. = 10^1$
1	$1. = \frac{1}{1}$
$\frac{1}{10}$	$0.1 = \frac{1}{10^1}$
$\frac{1}{10} \times \frac{1}{10}$	$0.01 = \frac{1}{10^2}$
$\frac{1}{10} \times \frac{1}{10} \times \frac{1}{10}$	$0.001 = \frac{1}{10^3}$

Discuss the convention used for writing powers of ten less than 1.

$$0.001 = \frac{1}{1000} = \frac{1}{10^3}$$

Lesson 4.6

TEACHING TIP Multiplying both the dividend and divisor by the same number before dividing can seem like hocus pocus to students, unless they are convinced that this really will not change the answer to the problem. To help convince students of this, have them complete the following problems.

$6 \div 1 = 6$
↓ Double divisor and dividend.
$12 \div 2 = 6$
↓ Double divisor and dividend.
$24 \div 4 = 6$

Doubling the value of both factors does not change the value of the answer. Students can also multiply two decimal numbers by the same number without changing the answer.

INCLUSION Students may forget whether they need to clear the decimal places from the dividend or the divisor. Remind them that they already know how to divide a decimal number by a whole number, but not how to divide a whole number by a decimal number. Therefore, they must make the divisor a whole number.

Lesson 4.7

COMMON ERROR Students often think that the units such as kilograms and grams are units of weight, because of the context in which they have seen these units used. Explain to them that mass measures the amount of matter in an object. Weight is the force exerted on the mass by gravity. Therefore, in outer space, an object becomes weightless, but its mass has not changed from what it was at sea level.

TEACHING TIP Collect easily recognized liquid containers of varying capacities (8 ounce milk container, 12 ounce juice can, pint container, quart container, 24 ounce juice bottle, half-gallon container, gallon container). Order the containers from least to greatest capacity. Have students make a table with a picture of each container. Record the capacity of each container in customary units. Next, have students measure and record the capacity of each container in milliliters. This will help students remember and understand the benchmark references and the meaning of capacity in the metric system.

Lesson 4.8

TEACHING TIP Teach students how to recall and write the metric units in order. Use the phrase:

King **H**enry **D**oesn't **U**sually **D**rink **C**old **M**ilk.

Each first letter matches the first letter of a metric unit.

Kilo-, **H**ecto-, **D**eka-, **U**NIT, **D**eci-, **C**enti-, **M**illi-

TEACHING TIP Remind students to use number sense when writing equivalent units. If they are changing a measure from a smaller unit of measure to a larger one, they need fewer of these larger units to make the same length, so they should divide. If they want to change from a larger unit to a smaller one, they will need more of these units, so they should multiply.

CHAPTER 4

Name _____ Date _____

Parents as Partners
Use with Chapter 4.

Chapter Overview One way you can help your student succeed in Chapter 4 is by discussing the lesson goals in the chart below. When a lesson is completed, ask your student the following questions. "What were the goals of the lesson? What new words and formulas did you learn? How can you apply the ideas of the lesson to your life?"

Lesson Title	Lesson Goals	Key Applications
4.1: Multiplying Decimals and Whole Numbers	Multiply decimals and whole numbers. Check answers for reasonableness. Use properties of multiplication.	• Iditarod Race • Bottled Water • Suits of Armor
4.2: The Distributive Property	Use the distributive property to evaluate expressions. Use a formula.	• Astronomy • Lunch Costs • U.S. Mint
4.3: Multiplying Decimals	Multiply decimals by decimals. Use a model to multiply decimals. Place a decimal point in a product. Find the area of a rectangle.	• American Flag • Hair Growth • Turtle Speed • Deli Foods
4.4: Dividing by Whole Numbers	Divide decimals by whole numbers. Write additional zeros in the dividend as needed.	• Sports Cards • Speed Skating • Compact Discs • Sky Tram
4.5: Multiplying and Dividing by Powers of Ten	Use mental math to help multiply and divide decimals by powers of ten.	• Bridges • Weaving • Ice Hockey
4.6: Dividing by Decimals	Divide by decimals. Write divisors as whole numbers.	• Pumpkin Boat Race • Photos • Gas Mileage
4.7: Mass and Capacity	Use metric units of mass and capacity	• Iced Tea • Mountain Climbing • Water Usage
4.8: Changing Metric Units	Change from one metric unit of measure to another. Compare measures. Use a verbal model.	• State Quarters • Sunflower Height • Bowling Balls

Know How to Take Notes

Previewing the Chapter is the strategy featured in Chapter 4 (see page 152). Encourage your student to read or at least skim through the material before the new lesson is taught. Familiar vocabulary words can be written down and their definitions and uses reviewed. New vocabulary can also be written down and their definitions previewed. Previewing the chapter in this way prepares your student to be more actively involved and helps prevent your student from becoming "lost" while the teacher presents new material.

Middle School Math, Course 1
Professional Development Book

CHAPTER 4 Continued

Parents as Partners
Use with Chapter 4.

Key Ideas Your student can demonstrate understanding of key concepts by working through the following exercises with you.

Lesson	Exercise
4.1	Find the product. Use estimation to check your answer. (a) 23.4 × 7 (b) 18 × 0.045
4.2	Use the distributive property to rewrite the expression. (a) 10(2.6 + 40.9) (b) 7(8.2) − 7(5) (c) 9(6.3)
4.3	Find the area of the top of a rectangular coffee table with length 1.4 meters and width 0.6 meter.
4.4	Divide. Round to the nearest tenth if necessary. (a) 12 ÷ 8 (b) 6 ÷ 9 (c) 8.1 ÷ 3
4.5	A woman divides $2.7 million into equal shares for each of her ten grandchildren. Write 2.7 million as a whole number, then find the value of each share.
4.6	You paid $12.97 for 3.25 pounds of cashews. Find the cost per pound.
4.7	Choose an appropriate metric unit to measure the item. (a) capacity of a medical syringe (b) mass of a baby (c) mass of a frozen fruit treat (d) capacity of an Olympic-sized pool
4.8	Arrange the masses in order from least to greatest. 31.6 grams, 4212 milligrams, 0.04 kilogram

Home Involvement Activity

Directions: Name four cities in the United States or Canada you would like to visit. Record the distance to each city using an atlas or a computer maps program. If you travel in a car at an average speed of 55 miles per hour, how long would it take to drive to each city? How much gasoline would be used for each trip? (*Hint:* You will need to know how many miles the car gets per gallon of gasoline.

Answers

4.1: (a) 163.8 (b) 0.81   4.2: (a) 10(2.6) + 10(40.9) (b) 7(8.2 − 5) (c) 9(6) + 9(0.3) or 9(6 + 0.3)   4.3: 0.84 m²   4.4: (a) 1.5 (b) 0.7 (c) 2.7   4.5: 2,700,000; $270,000   4.6: $3.99   4.7: (a) mL (b) kg (c) g (d) kL   4.8: 4212 mg, 31.6 g, 0.04 kg

CHAPTER 4

Bulletin Board Idea

Use with Chapter 4.

Objective

To visually reinforce the concepts of multiplying and dividing by powers of ten.

Materials

- construction paper
- photos of apples or farmstands from magazines
- apple stickers or stencil of an apple
- 3 sentence strips

Constructing the Bulletin Board

1. With construction paper, create a pictograph using the apple stickers or stencils. Use the data for apple sales at the Good Foods Farmstand for a period of 5 years in the table at the right. For decimals, use partial apples to represent 0.25, 0.5, and 0.75.

2. Place photos of apples or farmstands around the graph.

3. On the sentence strips, write the following questions.

Good Foods Farmstand Apple Sales, 1996–2000

Year	Sales (1000 pounds)
1996	2.75
1997	4.00
1998	4.25
1999	5.50
2000	5.25

- How many more pounds of apples did the farmstand sell in 1998 than in 1996? [1500 pounds]

- In which year were apple sales the greatest during the period 1996 to 2000? [1999]

- In 2001, the quantity of apples sold was 3500 pounds. How would you represent this data in the graph? [3.5 apples]

Using the Bulletin Board

After students complete Lesson 4.5, discuss the bulletin board and its questions with the class. Explain the rules for multiplying or dividing by powers of ten. The discussion and the solution to the problem may include the following points.

- An easy way to multiply decimals by powers of ten is to move the decimal point one place to the right for each zero in the power of 10.

- When data in a graph are expressed in powers of ten, the data in the graph must be multiplied by the power of ten given in the key to calculate the actual value. If adding or subtracting this type of data, you can add or subtract the decimal values, and then multiply the sum or difference by the power of ten.

Follow-up

- Have students find examples of other graphs that use powers of ten in magazines or newspapers and bring them into class. Display them around the room and discuss them with the class.

Middle School Math, Course 1
Professional Development Book

Chapter 5

Math Behind the Math

Use with Chapter 5.

Lessons 5.1–5.2

Chapter 5 explores the basic concepts of number theory, which is the branch of mathematics that explores the *counting numbers*. The counting numbers are the numbers 1, 2, 3, 4, and so on.

FACTORS The answer to a multiplication problem is called the *product*. The numbers that are multiplied are called the *factors*. For example, the factors of 12 are: 1, 2, 3, 4, 6, and 12. The product of the pairs of factors 1 and 12, 2 and 6, and 3 and 4 are equal to 12.

One way to classify whole numbers is by the number of factors they have. A *prime number* is a whole number that has only the numbers 1 and itself for factors. So, the numbers 2, 3, 5, 7, and 11 are all examples of prime numbers.

A *composite number*, such as 10, has factors other than 1 and itself.

Factors of 10: 1×10; 2×5 so 1, 2, 5, and 10 are factors.

The numbers 0 and 1 are neither prime nor composite numbers.

PRIME FACTORIZATION *Prime factorization* is the process used to find the prime factors of a number. In this year's math course, students will use prime factorization to find the Greatest Common Factor (GCF) or the Least Common Multiple (LCM) of two or more numbers.

The number 36 has nine factors: 1, 2, 3, 4, 6, 9, 12, 18, and 36. Its prime factors are 2 and 3. A factor tree is the simplest method for finding all the prime factors of a number.

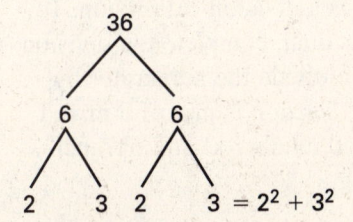

```
        36
       /  \
      6    6
     /\   /\
    2  3 2  3   = 2² + 3²
```

Lesson 5.3

FRACTIONS AND EQUIVALENCE A fraction is one way to express division. It is also one way to record a ratio. A fraction can represent parts of a whole or parts of a set. The shaded portion of both of these models represents $\frac{3}{4}$.

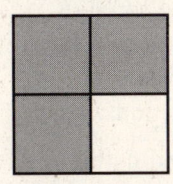

WRITING EQUIVALENT FRACTIONS Equivalent fractions have the same value—they represent the same number on a number line. Students may find it helpful to construct a number line that shows the relationship between equivalent fractions.

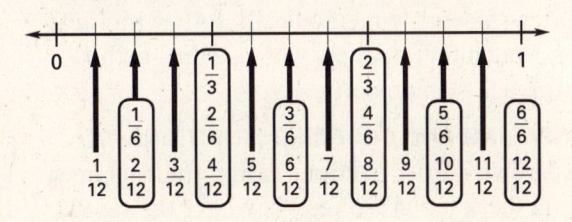

Recall that fractions that have the same number in the numerator and the denominator are equivalent to 1. To find an equivalent fraction, multiply by a fraction equivalent to 1.

$$\frac{1}{3} = \frac{1}{3} \times \frac{2}{2} = \frac{1 \times 2}{3 \times 2} = \frac{2}{6}$$

Students use the inverse operation, division, and the same essential process to simplify fractions.

SIMPLIFYING FRACTIONS Fractions are in simplest form when the numerator and denominator have no common factors. Since 5 and 6 in the fraction $\frac{5}{6}$ have no common factors, $\frac{5}{6}$ is in simplest form. Encourage students to simplify a fraction by looking for the greatest factor that the numerator and denominator have in common.

Lessons 5.4–5.5

MULTIPLES AND LEAST COMMON MULTIPLES
A *multiple* of a number is the product of a number and any nonzero whole number. For example, the multiples of 4 and 5 are the following.

4: 4, 8, 12, 16, **20**, 24, 28, 32, 36, **40** . . .

5: 5, 10, 15, **20**, 25, 30, 35, **40**, 45 . . .

The *common multiples* of 4 and 5 are 20, 40, 60, and so on.

Middle School Math, Course 1
Professional Development Book

CHAPTER 5 Continued
Math Behind the Math
Use with Chapter 5.

The *Least Common Multiple (LCM)* of two or more numbers is the least number that is a common multiple of the numbers. The LCM of 4 and 5 is 20. Because the LCM is used to write common denominators, it is helpful when comparing, adding, or subtracting fractions.

Lesson 5.4 shows two methods for finding the LCM. One method is the one described above. The second method is to first create factor trees for each number to obtain their prime factors. Then compare the factors and circle any common factors. Finally, multiply these common factors together to find the LCM. Note that this method requires students to methodically follow multiple steps. Watch that students who use this method follow each step properly.

COMPARING AND ORDERING FRACTIONS To compare and order fractions easily, students must rewrite the fractions so that they have the same denominators. To do this, students must find the *Least Common Denominator (LCD)*. The LCD of two or more fractions is the Least Common Multiple (LCM) of the denominators.

For example, to compare $\frac{3}{8}$, $\frac{2}{3}$, and $\frac{5}{6}$, use these steps.

- Find the LCM of the denominators.

  The LCD of $\frac{3}{8}$, $\frac{2}{3}$, and $\frac{5}{6}$ is 24.

- Write equivalent fractions using the LCD.

  $\frac{3 \times 3}{8 \times 3} = \frac{9}{24}$ $\frac{2 \times 8}{3 \times 8} = \frac{16}{24}$ $\frac{5 \times 4}{6 \times 4} = \frac{20}{24}$

Next, compare and order the numerators from least to greatest.

$9 < 16 < 20$

So, $\frac{9}{24} < \frac{16}{24} < \frac{20}{24}$, or $\frac{3}{8} < \frac{2}{3} < \frac{5}{6}$.

Lesson 5.6
CUSTOMARY MEASUREMENT AND FRACTIONS
The customary measures in use today are based on units of weights and measures that evolved in Great Britain and were used there until the mid-twentieth century. The customary system has many units of measure, such as the yard, foot, and pound. Because these units of measure are not related to each other by multiples of ten as in the metric system, fractions are often used.

MIXED NUMBERS AND IMPROPER FRACTIONS
A *mixed number* contains a whole-number part and a fraction part. An *improper fraction* is any fraction that *is equal to* or *greater than* 1.

The number sense behind the step-by-step procedure for rewriting mixed numbers as improper fractions and vice versa can be shown visually with a number line. The following model shows why the mixed number $4\frac{3}{5}$ can be written as the improper fraction $\frac{23}{5}$.

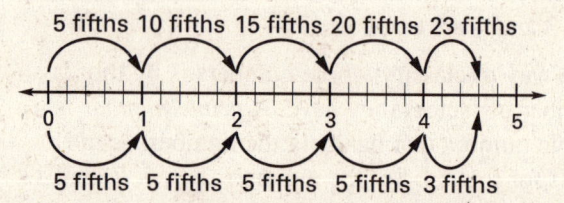

$4\frac{3}{5} = (4 \times 5 \text{ fifths}) + 3 \text{ fifths} = 20 \text{ fifths} + 3 \text{ fifths}$
$= \frac{23}{5}$

$\frac{23}{5} = (23 \div 5) = 4 \text{ wholes} + 3 \text{ fifths} = 4\frac{3}{5}$

Lessons 5.7–5.8
WRITING DECIMALS AS FRACTIONS Another name for a decimal is a decimal fraction. Decimal fractions and fractions are two ways to write parts of a whole.

Reading a decimal aloud or looking at a place-value chart will help students write decimals as fractions. When read aloud, the decimal 0.8 is *eight tenths*. Knowing this, students can easily write 0.8 as the fraction $\frac{8}{10}$. This fraction can then be simplified by dividing by the GCF. So, $\frac{8}{10}$ in simplest form is $\frac{4}{5}$.

WRITING FRACTIONS AS DECIMALS Recall that a fraction can be read as a division expression. To write a fraction as a decimal, complete the division shown by the fraction—divide the numerator by the denominator. If the fraction is part of a mixed number, write the mixed number as an improper fraction before dividing.

The two types of decimals describe the type of quotient obtained. The fraction $\frac{3}{6}$ equals the terminating decimal 0.5 because the answer terminates, or stops, at 5. The fraction $\frac{2}{3}$ equals the repeating decimal 0.666 . . . or $0.\overline{6}$ because the 6 repeats indefinitely in the answer.

Chapter 5

Tips for New Teachers

Use with Chapter 5.

Lesson 5.1

TEACHING TIP When students are looking for all the factors of a number, have them use an organized list, such as the one below. In addition to organizing their thinking, this type of list will signal students when all factors are found.

Find the Factors of 30

Step 1 Try 1. Since 30 ÷ 1 = 30, 1 and 30 are factors.

1   30

Step 2 Try 2. Since 30 ÷ 2 = 15, 2 and 15 are factors.

1   2   15   30

Step 3 Try 3. Since 30 ÷ 3 = 10, 3 and 10 are factors.

1   2   3   10   15   30

Step 4 Try 4 and 5. Since 30 ÷ 4 = 27 R2 and 30 ÷ 5 = 6, 4 is not a factor, but 5 and 6 are.

1   2   3   5   6   10   15   30

After students have used this method to find factors for several numbers, have them talk about the patterns they see. Students may notice that the factors are automatically ordered from least to greatest. They may also notice that any factors near the middle of the list are close in value. This information can signal students that they have successfully found all the factors.

COMMON ERROR Students may not factor completely all the numbers in their factor trees. Remind them to check over their work to be sure that the numbers in the bottom row of each factor tree are all prime numbers.

Lesson 5.2

COMMON ERROR When listing the factors of a number, students may neglect to include 1 and the number itself in the factor list. If they neglect to do this, they will not find any common factors for pairs such as 10 and 11, or 7 and 14.

COMMON ERROR When students use factor trees, sometimes the two trees will have no factors in common. Students will often say that the common factor is 0, but it is, in fact, 1. When two numbers have no common *prime* factors, they still have a common factor of 1.

INCLUSION You can help students visualize relationships between two numbers and their prime factors by using a table similar to the one below. Ask students to find the prime factors of 36 and 54 and record them in the table.

Prime factors of 36	Prime factors of both 36 and 54	Prime factors of 54
2 ·	2 · 3 · 3	· 3

The GCF is 2 · 3 · 3, or 18.

The product of the numbers in the first two boxes of the table is 36, and the product of the numbers in the second two boxes is 54. The product of the numbers in the center box, the factors common to both numbers, is the GCF.

Lesson 5.3

INCLUSION For your visual learners, show the elapsed times in Example 4 on a clock face. The solution in the text uses the 60 equal minutes in an hour to write fractions with a denominator of 60. With the clock face, students can also write the fractions using the 12 equal 5 minute intervals in an hour.

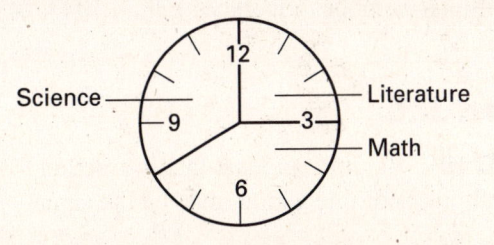

With this model, the fractions become

15 minutes = $\frac{3}{12}$ = $\frac{1}{4}$ hour

25 minutes = $\frac{5}{12}$ hour

20 minutes = $\frac{4}{12}$ = $\frac{1}{3}$ hour

TEACHING TIP When students are simplifying fractions, remind them that even if they did not use the greatest common factor, they need not

Chapter 5 Continued: Tips for New Teachers
Use with Chapter 5.

start over. Rather, they need to continue the process using another common factor. Point out that using the greatest common factor will allow them to finish with just one simplification.

Lesson 5.4

COMMON ERROR When identifying the least common multiple of two numbers, many students may simply multiply the two numbers. For example, to find a common multiple of 36 and 54, some students will multiply 36 and 54 to get 1944. Remind students that this will always give them a common multiple, but rarely will it be the *least* common multiple.

INCLUSION Displaying the prime factorization of two numbers in a table such as the one below can help students visualize the relationships between the two numbers and their LCM. For example, the table below can be used to find the LCM of 36 and 54.

Prime factors of 36	Prime factors of both 36 and 54	Prime factors of 54
2 ·	2 · 3 · 3	· 3

The LCM is 2 · 2 · 3 · 3 · 3, or 108.

The product of all the factors in the table is the LCM. In this example, the LCM is 108, which is a much simpler number to work with than 1944 (36 · 54).

Lesson 5.5

TEACHING TIP Remind students that in fraction models, all pieces of one whole must be the same size.

INCLUSION Have your visual students make models of the fractions in Example 1 by folding paper. To fold a sheet of paper to represent ninths, have students fold the paper in thirds lengthwise, and then in thirds widthwise. Ask students to trace over each fold and shade $\frac{7}{9}$ of the paper. Then have them fold a second sheet of paper to represent sixths. Ask students to trace over each fold and shade $\frac{5}{6}$ of the paper.

Next, help students place new folds in the $\frac{7}{9}$ model so that it represents $\frac{14}{18}$. Halving each ninth section will result in eighteen equal sections. Use this model to guide students in folding the model of $\frac{5}{6}$ so that it represents $\frac{15}{18}$.

Lesson 5.6

INCLUSION For students who get confused by mathematical symbolism, you can use a more verbal algorithm. For example, to write $2\frac{5}{8}$ as an improper fraction, use the following steps.

- $2\frac{5}{8}$ is 2 and 5 eighths.
- 2 wholes are 2 × 8 eighths, or 16 eighths.
- So, $2\frac{5}{8}$ is 16 eighths plus 5 eighths, or 21 eighths.

Lesson 5.7

TEACHING TIP Have students memorize the fraction/decimal equivalents listed in the margin of page 249. Knowing these equivalents will help students work quickly and confidently on standardized tests. You may want students to make flash cards with the fraction form on one side of the card and the decimal form on the other side.

TEACHING TIP To relate the skills of this lesson to those of the previous chapter, have students compare two decimals by comparing their fraction forms. They should see that writing two decimals so they have the same number of decimal places is equivalent to writing them with a common denominator.

Lesson 5.8

TEACHING TIP For Example 3, ask students how they can tell that the pattern of decimals will keep repeating. They should see that once the remainders start repeating, the digits in the quotient will also start repeating.

TEACHING TIP Have students use their calculators to find the decimal equivalents for each of the unit fractions $\frac{1}{2}, \frac{1}{3}, \frac{1}{4}, \ldots \frac{1}{20}$. Then have them go down the list and decide which decimals are repeating, which are terminating, and which cannot be determined from the digits on the calculator.

Middle School Math, Course 1
Professional Development Book

Chapter 5

Name _____ **Date** _____

Parents as Partners

Use with Chapter 5.

Chapter Overview One way you can help your student succeed in Chapter 5 is by discussing the lesson goals in the chart below. When a lesson is completed, ask your student the following questions. "What were the goals of the lesson? What new words and formulas did you learn? How can you apply the ideas of the lesson to your life?"

Lesson Title	Lesson Goals	Key Applications
5.1: Prime Factorization	Write whole numbers as the product of prime factors. Use divisibility rules. Classify as prime or composite.	• Dancers • Summer Camp • Marching Band • Relay Race
5.2: Greatest Common Factor	Find the greatest common factor of two or more numbers.	• Boat Tours • Parades • Museums
5.3: Equivalent Fractions	Write equivalent fractions. Simplify fractions.	• Movies • Beads • Chess
5.4: Least Common Multiple	Find least common multiples.	• Ferry Boats • Gift Certificates • Insects
5.5: Ordering Fractions	Compare and order fractions.	• Wrench Sizes • Gold Jewelry • Continent Areas
5.6: Mixed Numbers and Improper Fractions	Compare and order mixed numbers and improper fractions. Measure to a fraction of an inch.	• Industrial Arts • Baseball Bats • Pole Vaulting
5.7: Changing Decimals to Fractions	Write decimals as fractions. Write decimals as mixed numbers.	• Planets • Road Trip • Honeybees • Rainfall
5.8: Changing Fractions to Decimals	Write fractions as decimals. Write mixed numbers as decimals.	• Lighthouses • Watermelons • Gardening • Fishing

Know How to Take Notes

Learning Vocabulary is the strategy featured in Chapter 5 (see page 212). Encourage your student to learn the complete and accurate meanings of vocabulary words. Check to be sure that your student has written each vocabulary word, along with its definition and an example of how it is used, in his/her notebook. If the vocabulary word has more than one application, each one should be defined and illustrated. Have your student describe other examples to demonstrate and reinforce comprehension of the word(s).

CHAPTER 5 Continued

Name _____ Date _____

Parents as Partners
Use with Chapter 5.

Key Ideas Your student can demonstrate understanding of key concepts by working through the following exercises with you.

Lesson	Exercise
5.1	Write the prime factorization of the number 66.
5.2	There are 24 boys and 32 girls in the math club. You want to make teams of boys and teams of girls that all have the same number of members. What is the greatest number of members each team can have?
5.3	Write each fraction in simplest form. (a) $\frac{12}{30}$ (b) $\frac{15}{45}$ (c) $\frac{2}{26}$ (d) $\frac{120}{132}$
5.4	You visit your grandparents every third weekend. Your cousins visit your grandparents every eighth weekend. How often do you and your cousins visit your grandparents on the same weekend?
5.5	You need to loosen a bolt. A $\frac{5}{16}$ inch wrench is a little too big. Should you try a $\frac{1}{4}$ inch wrench or a $\frac{3}{8}$ inch wrench?
5.6	Write the mixed numbers as improper fractions and the improper fractions as mixed numbers. (a) $2\frac{1}{8}$ (b) $5\frac{3}{4}$ (c) $\frac{17}{6}$ (d) $\frac{23}{4}$
5.7	You boiled an egg for 5.75 minutes. Write the number of minutes as a mixed number.
5.8	The distance from your school to the public library is $2\frac{1}{3}$ kilometers. Write the number of kilometers as a repeating decimal.

Home Involvement Activity

Directions: Look through cook books, newspapers, and instruction manuals to find ten different fractions. Find the least common denominator for the group of ten fractions. Use the LCD to write equivalent fractions. Then arrange the fractions in order from least to greatest.

Answers

5.1: 2·3·11   5.2: 8   5.3: (a) $\frac{2}{5}$ (b) $\frac{1}{3}$ (c) $\frac{1}{13}$ (d) $\frac{10}{11}$ 5.4: every 24th weekend   5.5: $\frac{1}{4}$ inch wrench   5.6: (a) $\frac{17}{8}$ (b) $\frac{23}{4}$ (c) $2\frac{5}{6}$ (d) $5\frac{3}{4}$ 5.7: $5\frac{3}{4}$ minutes   5.8: 2.$\overline{3}$ km

62 Middle School Math, Course 1
Professional Development Book

CHAPTER 5

Bulletin Board Idea

Use with Chapter 5.

Objective

To visually reinforce the concepts of common multiples and least common multiples

Materials

- 3 sheets of construction paper
- 3 sentence strips
- yarn

Constructing the Bulletin Board

1. Enlarge the gear wheels below and copy each enlargement onto construction paper. Cut out the three gears and mount them on the bulletin board. Make sure that each pair of gears appears to be engaged. Draw a star on the tooth of each gear that is nearest to the point of contact. (The center gear will have two stars on it.)

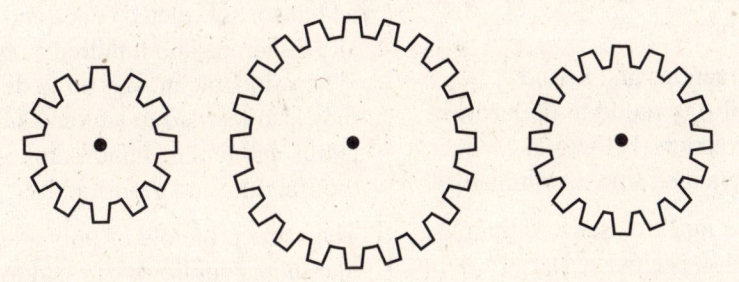

2. On one sentence strip, write the title, "Gears Make the World Go Round." On each of the other two sentence strips, write "How many rotations will each of these gears make before the two stars line up again?"

3. Place one question under each point of contact of the gears. Use yarn to make a pointer extending from each question to the point of contact above it. Around the board you may want to include photos of machinery containing gears.

Using the Bulletin Board

After students complete Lesson 5.4, discuss the bulletin board and its questions with the class. The discussion may include the following points.

- If one gear has fewer teeth than a second gear that is connected to it, then one revolution of the first gear will not produce a full revolution of the second gear. The second gear will rotate only through the same number of teeth as the first gear.

- Have students calculate how many teeth the smallest gear would need to move for its star to line up with the star of the middle gear again. (60 teeth). How many teeth would the middle sized gear need to move for that pair of stars to line up? (80 teeth). Then challenge them to find the number of teeth all three gears would need to move for both pair of stars to line up again. (240 teeth, or 12 revolutions of the center gear).

Follow-up

- Have students bring to class examples of gears that they have at home. Encourage them to bring in items, such as toys, in which the gears are visible. Have students make up problems about these gear ratios.

Chapter 6: Math Behind the Math

Use with Chapter 6.

Lesson 6.1

ESTIMATING WITH FRACTIONS When students learned to round whole numbers, they used the digit to the right of the place they were rounding to as the signal to round up or round down. The number 5 was used as the halfway number because it is halfway between 0 and 9. Numbers of 5 and greater rounded up, and numbers less than 5 rounded down.

Similarly, the fraction $\frac{1}{2}$ is the halfway number for fractions and mixed numbers. Fractions of $\frac{1}{2}$ or greater round up to 1 when rounding to the nearest whole number. With mixed numbers, fractions of $\frac{1}{2}$ or greater signal that the mixed number will round up to the next whole number.

When estimating with fractions and mixed numbers, it may be helpful to round to the nearest $\frac{1}{2}$. Look at the table of fractions below. The fractions in each row have the same denominator.

- When the numerator is much closer to 0 than the denominator, the fraction is close to 0.
- When the numerator is about one half the denominator, the fraction is close to $\frac{1}{2}$.
- When the numerator is close to the denominator, then the fraction is close to 1.

Close to 0	Close to $\frac{1}{2}$	Close to 1
$\frac{1}{10}$	$\frac{4}{10}$	$\frac{9}{10}$
$\frac{2}{9}$	$\frac{5}{9}$	$\frac{10}{9}$
$\frac{5}{88}$	$\frac{43}{88}$	$\frac{79}{88}$
$\frac{3}{20}$	$\frac{11}{20}$	$\frac{17}{20}$

Once students understand the relative value of fractions, they can more easily calculate fractional sums and differences. For example, they can quickly estimate that the addition expression $4\frac{1}{8} + 2\frac{3}{4}$ will have a sum of about 7 by rounding $4\frac{1}{8}$ to 4 and $2\frac{3}{4}$ to 3. When they complete the calculation and get $6\frac{7}{8}$ as an answer, they can be confident that their answer is reasonable.

There will be some fractions whose values rest ambiguously between $\frac{1}{2}$ and a whole number. For example, the fraction $\frac{7}{9}$ can be estimated as $\frac{1}{2}$ or 1. Encourage students not to worry about which estimate to use. For a fraction such as this, either $\frac{1}{2}$ or 1 will lead to a reasonable estimate. The key idea is to use this estimation method to develop number sense and to help students work confidently and accurately with fraction computations.

Lessons 6.2–6.3

ADDING AND SUBTRACTING FRACTIONS When students first learned to add and subtract, they learned that they could only combine apples with apples, and oranges with oranges. Translated into the place-value system, this means that they only added (or subtracted) ones and ones, tens and tens, and hundreds and hundreds, regrouping as needed. When students moved on to decimal fractions, they also learned to add and subtract like things— tenths and tenths, hundredths and hundredths, thousandths and thousandths.

The same principle of only adding or subtracting like things applies when adding and subtracting fractions. The denominators are the "like things" that are being added or subtracted. Writing computations using labels for the denominators signals that it is the number of like things (in the numerators) that are added or subtracted, not the type of like things.

$$\frac{3}{5} \qquad \text{3 fifths}$$
$$+\frac{1}{5} \qquad +\text{ 1 fifth}$$
$$\overline{\frac{4}{5}} \qquad \overline{\text{4 fifths}}$$

Some students mistakenly add the denominators as well as the numerators. For example, some students may add $\frac{3}{10}$ to $\frac{5}{10}$ and write $\frac{8}{20}$ as the sum. You can use a related decimal expression to help students see why this is not correct. Ask students to write each fraction as its decimal equivalent and then add. The answer is 0.8, or 8 tenths.

0.3	3 tenths	$\frac{3}{10}$
+ 0.5	+ 5 tenths	+ $\frac{5}{10}$
0.8	8 tenths	$\frac{8}{10}$

64 Middle School Math, Course 1
Professional Development Book

Math Behind the Math

Use with Chapter 6.

When students add or subtract fractions in which the denominators are not the same, remind them to rewrite the fractions so that each fraction has the same denominator.

Lessons 6.4–6.5

ADDING AND SUBTRACTING MIXED NUMBERS

In these lessons in particular, ask all students to develop a consistent recording method for the addition and subtraction of mixed numbers. The stepwise checklist shown below can serve this purpose. Students can use the support of checklists such as this one until they feel confident about correctly following the multiple steps needed to add or subtract mixed numbers.

Mixed Number Subtraction Checklist

Step 1 Ask: **Do the fractions have the same denominators?**

If no, then use the LCD to rewrite the fractions.

$$3\frac{2}{5} \qquad \frac{2}{5} \times \frac{2}{2} = \frac{4}{10}$$
$$-1\frac{1}{2} \qquad \frac{1}{2} \times \frac{5}{5} = \frac{5}{10}$$

Step 2 Ask: **Can I subtract numerators?**

If no, then rename a whole. In this example, rename 1 as $\frac{4}{10} + \frac{10}{10}$, or $\frac{14}{10}$.

$$\overset{2}{\cancel{3}}\frac{4}{10} \qquad \frac{4}{10} + \frac{10}{10} = \frac{14}{10}$$
$$-1\frac{5}{10}$$

Step 3 Rewrite the problem and subtract.

$$2\frac{14}{10}$$
$$-1\frac{5}{10}$$

Step 4 Ask: **Is the answer in simplest form?**

If no, then simplify.

The answer in simplest form is $1\frac{9}{10}$.

Often students rush through the exercise sets for mixed numbers because adding and subtracting fractions less than one in Lesson 6.3 was easy for them. After all, adding $\frac{1}{5}$ and $\frac{3}{5}$ to get $\frac{4}{5}$ is, in essence, adding 1 and 3 to get 4, a skill that students mastered at a very young age.

Because of this, many students assume there is little need to record their work. When denominators are multiples of one another, they often attempt to rewrite problems mentally. This process works for some students, but many students make simple computation errors.

Computations become more challenging when adding and subtracting mixed numbers and when whole numbers need to be renamed. What was once a one- or two-step process becomes a multi-step process. Support students in the process until they can follow and record each step successfully.

Lesson 6.6

RENAMING TIME Whether a length of time is expressed as 90 minutes or 1 hour 30 minutes, it is still the same length of time. Just as you rename to add or subtract fractions, you can rename one greater unit of time for an equivalent number of a smaller unit of time.

Students can rename 1 hour as 60 minutes, 1 minute as 60 seconds, and 1 year as 365 days. Students must keep in mind that time units are not part of the base-ten system. Renaming time units is based on the number of lesser units that equal the greater unit. For example, to rename the minuend below, you do not regroup 100 minutes, but 60 minutes, because 1 hour = 60 minutes.

$$\cancel{5} \text{ h } 15 \text{ min}$$
$$- 2 \text{ h } 45 \text{ min}$$

↓

$$4 \text{ h} + 1 \text{ h } 15 \text{ min}$$
$$- 2 \text{ h} \qquad 45 \text{ min}$$

↓

$$4 \text{ h } 75 \text{ min}$$
$$- 2 \text{ h } 45 \text{ min}$$
$$ 2 \text{ h } 30 \text{ min}$$

CHAPTER 6: Tips for New Teachers

Use with Chapter 6.

Lesson 6.1

INCLUSION Some students may be unfamiliar with the symbol ≈. It is read "is approximately equal to." It usually indicates that a rounded number has been used in a calculation.

TEACHING TIP Emphasize to students that fractions and mixed numbers are rounded to make them easy to work with mentally. This usually means to the nearest $\frac{1}{2}$, but occasionally other fractions may be useful, depending on the context.

Lesson 6.2

COMMON ERROR Students who are confused about what a fraction represents may try to add denominators as well as numerators. When students do this, explain that the *denominator* of a fraction only describes the size of the pieces being added or subtracted, just as the *denomination* of paper currency describes how much it is worth. Students can work with denominators much like they do a unit of measure. For example, to add $\frac{3}{5}$ and $\frac{4}{5}$, they can think of the sum in the following terms.

3 fifths + 4 fifths = 7 fifths

Because 5 fifths = 1, 7 fifths = $1\frac{2}{5}$.

TEACHING TIP Have students compare the two equations in each Notebook feature. Be sure students understand that the algebraic equations are similar to the formulas they used earlier in the year. In each equation, any whole number can be substitutes for the variables *a*, *b*, and *c*, except $c = 0$.

Hands-on Activity 6.3

TEACHING TIP In the sum that is modeled, the paper is folded vertically to represent the first fraction and horizontally to represent the second. Students should follow the same procedure when modeling the exercises. When students add the shaded parts of the models, make sure students count every area. For example, for Exercise 2, students should count $\frac{6}{16}$ plus $\frac{8}{16}$ as $\frac{14}{16}$. They can then simplify $\frac{14}{16}$ to $\frac{7}{8}$.

Lesson 6.3

INCLUSION When adding and subtracting fractions, many students will want to use the product of the two denominators as the common denominator. Remind students that this method will work, but looking for the least common denominator will make their work go faster.

TEACHING TIP Encourage students to estimate each answer before they compute. This process will often help students identify and self-correct mistakes, such as using the incorrect operation.

Lesson 6.4

TEACHING TIP This lesson ties together many skills that students learned in earlier lessons. For example, the following skills are used in Example 2.

Find the sum: $2\frac{1}{12} + 1\frac{3}{4}$

$= 2 + \frac{1}{12} + 1 + \frac{3}{4}$ Definition of mixed number

$= (2 + 1) + \left(\frac{1}{12} + \frac{3}{4}\right)$ Commutative property

$= 3 + \left(\frac{1}{12} + \frac{3}{4}\right)$ Adding basic facts

$= 3 + \left(\frac{1}{12} + \frac{9}{12}\right)$ Writing equivalent fractions

$= 3 + \frac{10}{12}$ Adding fractions

$= 3 + \frac{5}{6}$ Simplifying fractions

$= 3\frac{5}{6}$

TEACHING TIP Many students fail to "take their space." This means they cram multi-step problems into tight spaces or fail to write the multiple steps down for fear of "wasting paper."

Ask students to fold their homework paper into eighths. Each space should be used for one exercise within the practice set. This technique can help reduce errors, increase handwriting legibility, and provide students an opportunity to look back and check their work if they incorrectly solve a problem.

CHAPTER 6 Continued

Tips for New Teachers
Use with Chapter 6.

Hands-on Activity 6.5

TEACHING TIP When students subtract mixed numbers, they need to compare fractions to decide whether or not renaming is needed. The models in this lesson make the comparisons visually apparent, so students may not notice they are using this skill. Point out to students that this skill is part of the process.

Lesson 6.5

COMMON ERROR When subtracting mixed numbers, students often try to subtract the lesser fraction from the greater when they should be renaming. Remind these students that subtraction is not commutative. Students need to find a way to get more fractional parts before subtracting. They can do this by renaming one whole as a fraction. You may want to compare this process to regrouping when subtracting decimal fractions.

INCLUSION When subtracting mixed numbers, some students drop a step when renaming a whole. To avoid this, you may want to teach students how to cancel a whole and record its fraction equivalent in the following manner.

Rename $5\frac{4}{12}$. Cross out the 5 and record a 4. Write $\frac{12}{12}$ at right.

$$\begin{array}{c} \cancel{5}\frac{4}{12} \\ -3\frac{9}{12} \end{array} \longrightarrow \begin{array}{c} \cancel{5}^{4}\frac{4}{12} + \frac{12}{12} = \frac{16}{12} \\ -3\frac{9}{12} \end{array}$$

Rewrite the problem and subtract.

$$\begin{array}{c} 4\frac{16}{12} \\ -3\frac{9}{12} \end{array}$$

The solution is $1\frac{7}{12}$.

TEACHING TIP You may want to present a few examples in which students must first decide whether they need to rename before subtracting. Otherwise, they may confront this decision process for the first time in a testing situation.

Lesson 6.6

COMMON ERROR Students often regroup 1 hour as 100 minutes instead of 60. Remind students that an hour has only 60 minutes. Asking students to estimate before they subtract is also helpful. In Example 2, for example, have students estimate the difference to the nearest half hour, which is 2 hours. Then if they try to subtract 117 minutes from 10 hours, their answer is 2 hours 75 minutes, which is over 3 hours and not reasonable.

INCLUSION To help students calculate elapsed time for Example 3, you may want them to draw a clock with the initial time showing. Have them count the hours until 4:15 P.M. Then have students add to this sum the extra minutes that are needed to get to 4:22 P.M.

Encourage your kinesthetic learners to compute elapsed time by using their fingers to touch a table. For example, to count the elapsed hours between 6:00 A.M. and 11:00 A.M., try this method.

Say, "6:00 to 7:00."	Touch pinkie to table.
Say, "7:00 to 8:00."	Touch ring finger to table.
Say, "8:00 to 9:00."	Touch middle finger to table.
Say, "9:00 to 10:00."	Touch pointing finger to table.
Say, "10:00 to 11:00."	Touch thumb to table.

Now count the number of fingers touching the table. There are five fingers touching, so 5 hours passed between 6:00 A.M. and 11:00 A.M.

CHAPTER 6

Name _____ **Date** _____

Parents as Partners

Use with Chapter 6.

Chapter Overview One way you can help your student succeed in Chapter 6 is by discussing the lesson goals in the chart below. When a lesson is completed, ask your student the following questions. "What were the goals of the lesson? What new words and formulas did you learn? How can you apply the ideas of the lesson to your life?"

Lesson Title	Lesson Goals	Key Applications
6.1: Fraction Estimation	Estimate with fractions and mixed numbers. Round fractions and mixed numbers.	• Gecko size • Costumes • Long Lines • Rockets
6.2: Fractions with Common Denominators	Find actual sums and differences of fractions.	• Baking Cookies • Swim Relay Race • Online Time Surveys
6.3: Fractions with Different Denominators	Add and subtract with different denominators.	• Activities • Rainfall • Obstacle Course • Appalachian Trail
6.4: Adding and Subtracting Mixed Numbers	Add and subtract mixed numbers.	• Sculpture • Volcano • Skis • Old Currency
6.5: Subtracting Mixed Numbers by Renaming	Subtract mixed numbers by renaming.	• Horses • Unicycles • Snake Length
6.6: Measures of Time	Add and subtract measures of time. Find elapsed time.	• Tour de France • Winter Solstice • Snorkeling • Time Zones

Know How to Take Notes

Writing a Summary is the strategy featured in Chapter 6 (see page 266). Encourage your student to summarize each chapter in his/her own words. Your student can use the lesson headings as a guide to help create an outline. This outline can then be completed using the key concepts and examples from each lesson. Your student should also include additional explanations, hints, or tips given by the teacher that aid in comprehension of the chapter.

Chapter 6 Continued

Name _____ **Date** _____

Parents as Partners

Use with Chapter 6.

Key Ideas Your student can demonstrate understanding of key concepts by working through the following exercises with you.

Lesson	Exercise
6.1	You need to be at least 4 feet tall to go on all the rides at a local amusement park. Right now you are $45\frac{1}{4}$ inches tall. Estimate how many inches you need to grow to be able to go on all of the rides.
6.2	A small loaf of apple bran bread requires $\frac{3}{4}$ cup of peeled and chopped apples and $\frac{3}{4}$ cup of whole wheat flour. Find the sum. Simplify if possible.
6.3	A sourdough bread recipe calls for $\frac{1}{2}$ cup water and $\frac{1}{3}$ cup yogurt. How much more water is needed than yogurt in the recipe?
6.4	The second-place jumper in a standing long jump competition had a jump of $80\frac{1}{2}$ inches. The winner jumped $2\frac{1}{4}$ inches farther. What was the distance of the winning jump?
6.5	The third-place jump in the standing long jump competition (from the Lesson 6.4 question) was $6\frac{1}{2}$ inches shorter than the second-place jump. What was the distance of the third-place jump?
6.6	You had four hours to complete your chores before your friend's parent was going to pick you up to go to a movie. It took you 1 hour and 10 minutes to mow the lawn. It took you 2 hours and 37 minutes to clean your room. Were you ready in time? How much earlier or later did you finish your chores than your ride was to arrive?

Home Involvement Activity

Directions: Find out how tall you were at birth and at the ages of three months, six months, and one year old (or you can use heights from any four ages). Next, find out how much you grew between birth and three months, three and six months, and six months and one year (or between the other ages you chose.) Find the sum of these three "growths" to see how much you grew during your first year (or other time period) of your life. (If you have no record of your own height, average heights for people of different ages can be found in an encyclopedia or on the Internet.)

Answers

6.1: About 3 inches   6.2: $\frac{4}{6} = \frac{3}{2} = 1\frac{1}{2}$ cups   6.3: $\frac{1}{6}$ 6.4: $82\frac{2}{2}$ in.   6.5: $73\frac{3}{4}$ in.   6.6: Yes, 13 minutes before your friend's parent was to arrive.

Middle School Math, Course 1
Professional Development Book
69

CHAPTER 6

Bulletin Board Idea

Use with Chapter 6.

Objective

To visually reinforce the concepts of adding and subtracting fractions

Materials

- construction paper
- covers from CDs (optional)
- 5 index cards
- 4 sentence strips

Constructing the Bulletin Board

1. Copy the circle graph below onto a large sheet of construction paper and place it on the bulletin board. On the index cards, create labels for the type of musical CD represented by each wedge, and the fraction of the total inventory it represents. Position each label on or beside its corresponding wedge.

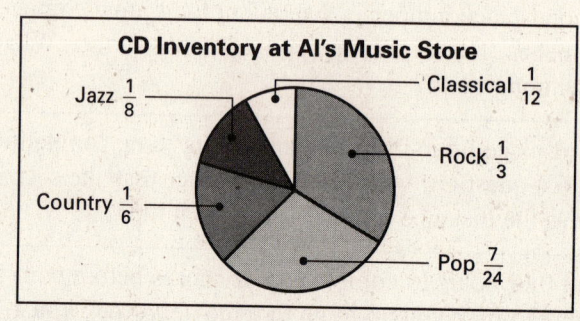

CD Inventory at Al's Music Store

Jazz $\frac{1}{8}$ — Classical $\frac{1}{12}$ — Rock $\frac{1}{3}$ — Country $\frac{1}{6}$ — Pop $\frac{7}{24}$

2. If possible, place a few CD covers beside the appropriate type of music.
3. On three sentence strips, write the following questions.
   - What fraction of the total inventory are rock and pop CDs?
   - How much more of the total inventory are pop CDs than country CDs?
   - What fraction of the inventory includes music you like?

Using the Bulletin Board

After students have completed Lesson 6.3, discuss the bulletin board and its questions with the class. The discussion may include the following points.

- The fraction of the inventory that comprises each type of music can be calculated by dividing the number of CDs of that type by the total number of CDs in the inventory and writing the fraction in simplest form.

- The sum of all the fractions in the circle graph should equal one. If you knew the total number of CDs in the inventory, you could calculate the number of CDs of each type.

Follow-up

- Have students go to a local music store and estimate the fraction of the total inventory for each type of music that the store carries.

CHAPTER 7

Math Behind the Math

Use with Chapter 7.

Lessons 7.1–7.2

MULTIPLYING FRACTIONS BY A WHOLE NUMBER

Multiplication is another way of adding a given number of equal quantities. When students first learned to multiply whole numbers, they used repeated addition. For example,

$$2 + 2 + 2 = 3 \times 2,\text{ and}$$

$$4 \times \frac{3}{4} = \frac{3}{4} + \frac{3}{4} + \frac{3}{4} + \frac{3}{4} = \frac{12}{4} = 3$$

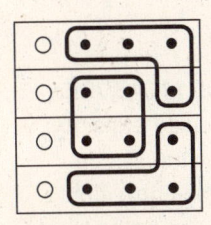

The model above connects repeated addition to multiplication with fractions. Some students do not believe the product is 3 until they cut out the 4 groups of $\frac{3}{4}$ and rearrange them to make 3 wholes. Allow students the opportunity to complete several problems in this way.

Once students use these methods and find several products, they gladly accept the numerical method for multiplying fractions as a shortcut.

$$4 \times \frac{3}{4} = 4 \times 3 \text{ fourths} = 12 \text{ fourths}$$

$$\frac{12}{4} = 3$$

Students can check the reasonableness of products by rounding fractions to the nearest 0, $\frac{1}{2}$, or 1. In the problem $4 \times \frac{3}{4} = \frac{12}{4} = 3$, the fraction $\frac{3}{4}$ is close to 1, so round up. The estimate is 4×1, or 4.

The fraction is rounded up, so the actual answer is less than 4. Whenever students multiply a fraction less than 1 and a whole number, they should expect that the product will be less than the whole number. This is because they are finding only part of the whole.

For many students, the procedures for multiplying fractions are deceptively easy. After all the rewriting, renaming, and simplifying they needed to do in the addition and subtraction of fractions, students often wonder if they have actually multiplied properly.

The identity property allows any whole number to be written as a fraction with a denominator of 1.

$$\frac{4}{1} \times \frac{3}{4} = \frac{12}{4} = 3$$

Some students may enjoy the simplicity of writing the whole number with a denominator of 1 and then using the multiplication rule to find the product.

Rule for Multiplying Fractions:

Multiply numerators to find the numerator.
Multiply denominators to find the denominator.

MULTIPLYING FRACTIONS LESS THAN ONE

Students have seen how a 3-row by 4-column array model shows the multiplication of the whole number 12. Array models can help explain why the rule for multiplying fractions less than one works.

This is 1 whole.

To model $\frac{3}{4} \times \frac{2}{3}$, divide the whole into fourths vertically and into thirds horizontally.

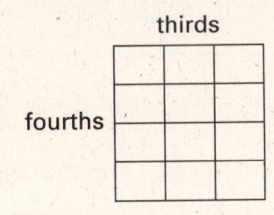

The whole is now divided into twelfths. Each small square is $\frac{1}{12}$ of the whole. The problem $\frac{3}{4} \times \frac{2}{3}$ can be read as "What is $\frac{3}{4}$ of $\frac{2}{3}$?" Students have to find a fraction of a fraction.

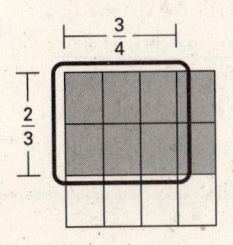

Middle School Math, Course 1
Professional Development Book

Math Behind the Math

Use with Chapter 7.

Shade $\frac{2}{3}$ of the rectangle. The shaded area represents $\frac{2}{3}$. To find $\frac{3}{4}$ of $\frac{2}{3}$, select $\frac{3}{4}$ of the shaded area. The selected area represents $\frac{3}{4}$ of $\frac{2}{3}$. When you count the number of small squares, you find this area equals $\frac{6}{12}$. So, $\frac{3}{4}$ of $\frac{2}{3}$ is $\frac{6}{12}$, or $\frac{1}{2}$.

$$\frac{3}{4} \times \frac{2}{3} = \frac{6}{12} = \frac{1}{2}$$

When multiplying two fractions that are each less than 1, the product is always less than 1 because the multiplication takes place within that 1 whole. Because you are finding part of a part, the product will be less than either fraction.

Lesson 7.3

MIXED NUMBER MULTIPLICATION Array models can show multiplication of mixed numbers as well as fractions. The following array is another way to model the multiplication problem in the activity on page 326. The problem can be read as "What is $\frac{1}{2}$ of $1\frac{1}{3}$?"

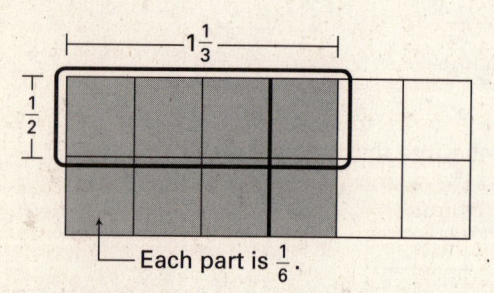

Each part is $\frac{1}{6}$.

$$\frac{1}{2} \times 1\frac{1}{3} \longrightarrow \frac{1}{2} \times \frac{4}{3} = \frac{4}{6} = \frac{2}{3}$$

Lessons 7.4–7.5

FRACTION DIVISION When dividing whole numbers, fractions less than 1, or mixed numbers, it helps to visualize fractional parts by drawing a quick sketch of the question being asked. It also helps students to read the problem aloud and translate the division expression into words. For example, in the problem $3 \div \frac{3}{8}$, ask, "How many groups of $\frac{3}{8}$ are in 3?"

When you divide by a fraction, multiply by the reciprocal of the divisor.

$$3 \div \frac{3}{8} = 3 \times \frac{8}{3} = \frac{24}{3} = 8$$

When you break 3 wholes into eighths, you have 24 eighths. You divide the 24 eighths into groups of 3 eighths. There are 8 groups of $\frac{3}{8}$.

$$24 \text{ eighths} \div 3 \text{ eighths} = \frac{24 \text{ eighths}}{3 \text{ eighths}} = 8$$

Lessons 7.6–7.7

CHANGING CUSTOMARY UNITS OF MEASURE
Customary units of length, weight, and capacity are not part of the base-ten place-value system. Encourage students to memorize the equivalent measures for customary measures shown on page 350. Knowing the relationships between units, such as 12 inches = 1 foot, will be essential when students solve measurement problems. Consider the following problem.

Mark is 4 feet 10 inches tall. Ajeet is 63 inches tall. Who is taller?

To compare these two heights, first write each boy's height using the same units, either inches or feet plus inches. Then compare.

Write both heights in inches.

1 ft = 12 in.   Write ft : in. relationship.

(4 ft **×** 12) + 10 = 58 in.   Multiply.

Mark is 58 inches tall. Ajeet is 63 inches tall.

Or, write both heights in feet plus inches.

1 ft = 12 in.   Write ft : in. relationship.

63 ÷ **12 in.** = 5 ft 3 in.   Divide.

Mark is 4 feet 10 inches tall. Ajeet is 5 feet 3 inches tall.

Either way, students can compare the two heights. Ajeet is taller than Mark.

CHAPTER 7 — Tips for New Teachers

Use with Chapter 7.

Lesson 7.1

INCLUSION For your kinesthetic learners, have students make the models in the activity from sheets of paper. Students can then cut off the shaded thirds from two of the squares and place them on the unshaded parts of the four other wholes. This will physically show that the four wholes represent the answer.

INCLUSION For students who are acquiring English, discuss the connection between the word *of* and multiplying whole numbers. For example, 3 boxes *of* 8 crayons can be represented as 3×8 crayons. Similarly, $\frac{3}{4}$ *of* 8 crayons can be written as $\frac{3}{4} \times 8$ crayons.

Encourage all students to read expressions such as $\frac{3}{4} \times 8$ crayons as a word expression, "$\frac{3}{4}$ of 8 crayons." When students understand that they need to find $\frac{3}{4}$ of 8 crayons, many will think, "I know $\frac{1}{2}$ of 8 crayons is 4, and since $\frac{3}{4}$ is a bit more, then $\frac{3}{4}$ of 8 crayons is about 6 crayons."

Lesson 7.2

TEACHING TIP Plan to spend most of the class period on Example 1. The model shows clearly and simply how to find a fractional part of a fraction. Once students understand that a fraction *of* a fraction is the same as a fraction *times* a fraction, multiplying fractions becomes concrete and visual. The model will help students with many common stumbling blocks, such as why the product of two fractions is less than either factor, even though the product of two whole numbers is greater than either factor.

COMMON ERROR When students are multiplying three or more fractions, they might easily skip over one factor, especially if they have simplified first and have crossed out several factors. Have students rewrite these problems before multiplying, checking to see that all factors of the numerator and denominator are accounted for.

COMMON ERROR Emphasize to students that if they are going to simplify fractions before multiplying, they must simplify one number in the numerator and one number in the denominator.

For example, when multiplying $\frac{1}{6}$ and $\frac{7}{12}$, some students will want to simplify the numbers 6 and 12. However, because both these numbers are in the denominator and no numerator is divisible by 6, 2, or 3, this expression cannot be simplified.

TEACHING TIP Students may not understand why fractions can be simplified before multiplying. Remind them that they already know how to simplify by dividing out common factors after finding the product. However, they can divide out the common factors first. Then they have simpler number to multiply and will not need to simplify after they have multiplied.

Lesson 7.3

TEACHING TIP Point out to students that in the activity, once again they are interpreting $\times$ as the word *of*.

COMMON ERROR Students will often try to multiply two mixed numbers, as in Example 2, by first multiplying the whole numbers and then multiplying the fractions. However,

$$2\frac{2}{9} \times 4\frac{4}{5} \neq 2 \cdot 4 + \frac{2}{9} \cdot \frac{4}{5}$$

To find the correct product, they must also add to these two partial products two more partial products: $4 \cdot \frac{2}{9}$ and $2 \cdot \frac{4}{5}$. Finding the sum of all four partial products is cumbersome but will give the correct answer. However, it is usually easier to multiply the two improper fractions.

Hands-on Activity 7.4

TEACHING TIP If you create additional division examples for students, be sure the dividend is a multiple of the divisor's numerator. This will make the quotient a whole number.

Lesson 7.4

INCLUSION For students who are acquiring English, you may want to discuss the everyday usage of the word *reciprocal* and related words, such as *reciprocate*. To *reciprocate* a favor is to do a favor in return for a favor that someone did for you, so that neither person owes the other. In

Middle School Math, Course 1   73
Professional Development Book

Chapter 7 Continued: Tips for New Teachers

Use with Chapter 7.

essence, you are both back to the point at which you started. In the same way, multiplying a number *n* by a fraction and its reciprocal brings you back to the number *n*.

TEACHING TIP When multiplying by a reciprocal in a division problem does not make sense to students, use a verbal model to help explain. Think of the denominators as similar to units of measure, because their function is to describe the size of the fractional part being used. Example 3b can be solved as shown.

$$6 \div \frac{3}{4} = (6 \times 4) \text{ fourths} \div 3 \text{ fourths}$$
$$= 24 \text{ fourths} \div 3 \text{ fourths}$$
$$= 8$$

So, to divide 6 by $\frac{3}{4}$, you must first multiply 6 by 4, and then divide by 3. This is the same process as finding $6 \times \frac{4}{3}$.

Lesson 7.5

TEACHING TIP When mixed numbers have a common denominator, as in Example 1, you can use a verbal model to divide.

$$3\frac{1}{3} \div \frac{2}{3} = 10 \text{ thirds} \div 2 \text{ thirds}$$
$$= \frac{10 \text{ thirds}}{2 \text{ thirds}}, \text{ or } 5$$

This method can also be adapted for quotients with different denominators, such as in Exercise 2 on page 340. Begin by writing the fractions with a common denominator.

$$6\frac{2}{3} \div \frac{8}{9} = 20 \text{ thirds} \div 8 \text{ ninths}$$
$$= 60 \text{ ninths} \div 8 \text{ ninths}$$
$$= 7 \text{ R}(4 \text{ ninths})$$

To interpret the remainder, you need to rewrite 4 ninths as a fraction part of 8 ninths. Since 4 ninths is $\frac{1}{2}$ of 8 ninths, the answer is $7\frac{1}{2}$.

COMMON ERROR Some students may write the reciprocal of $2\frac{2}{3}$ as $2\frac{3}{2}$. Remind students that a mixed number has a reciprocal that is less than 1. They need to find the reciprocal of the entire mixed number, not just its fraction part.

Lesson 7.6

INCLUSION Since most of the world uses the metric system, students acquiring English may not be familiar with customary units of measure. To help these students make these units part of their vocabulary, post on the bulletin board photos of objects that have a measure of 1 ounce, 1 pound, 1 pint, 1 quart, and so on.

TEACHING TIP Some students may wonder how *ounces* and *fluid ounces* are related. The weight of one fluid ounce of water at normal temperature and pressure equals one "dry" ounce. This is the meaning behind the familiar verse "A pint's a pound the world around." Traditionally, on balance scales, 16 ounces of water was used to set the standard for 16 ounces (1 pound) of any dry good, such as a pound of rice. Be sure to emphasize that this relationship is for estimation purposes only. Density makes a difference! Other fluids will weigh slightly more or less, depending on their densities.

Lesson 7.7

TEACHING TIP For Example 2, emphasize the careful interpretation of the remainder for this type of problem. Ask students to think, "How many pounds are in 35 ounces?" Many students write 2 remainder 3 without thinking about what the 3 represents. If they write the 3 over 16, they begin to see the remainder as part of a pound. Watch for students who write answers such as 2.3 pounds. Recall $\frac{3}{16}$ is 0.1875. The answer is either 2 pounds 3 ounces, $2\frac{3}{16}$ pounds, or 2.1875 pounds.

TEACHING TIP Examples 3 and 4 introduce students to *dimensional analysis*, a technique used in the physical sciences. Dimensional analysis is based on the idea that 12 inches ÷ 3 inches = 4, not 4 inches. Written in fraction form, this statement becomes $\frac{12 \text{ inches}}{3 \text{ inches}} = 4$. So, students can think of this as dividing out a common unit, just as they divided out common factors.

CHAPTER 7

Name _____ Date _____

Parents as Partners
Use with Chapter 7.

Chapter Overview One way you can help your student succeed in Chapter 7 is by discussing the lesson goals in the chart below. When a lesson is completed, ask your student the following questions. "What were the goals of the lesson? What new words and formulas did you learn? How can you apply the ideas of the lesson to your life?"

Lesson Title	Lesson Goals	Key Applications
7.1: Multiplying Fractions and Whole Numbers	Multiply fractions and whole numbers. Use mental math or a model. Estimate a product.	• Party Music • CD Rack • National Parks • Travel Postcards
7.2: Multiplying Fractions	Multiply fractions.	• Scooter Sales • Soap Bubbles • Fingernails • Glaciers
7.3: Multiplying Mixed Numbers	Multiply mixed numbers.	• Trampoline • Soccer • Geometry
7.4: Dividing Fractions	Write reciprocals. Use reciprocals to divide fractions.	• Caves • Magnets • Clay Cups and Mugs
7.5: Dividing Mixed Numbers	Divide mixed numbers. Choose an operation by thinking of a similar problem.	• Cider • Volunteer Work • Alligators • Talent Show
7.6: Weight and Capacity in Customary Units	Use customary units of weight and capacity.	• Bakery • Animals • Hang Glider
7.7: Changing Customary Units	Change customary units of measure. Multiply by a form of 1. Find a relationship. Add and subtract measurements.	• Camels • Model Trains • Maple Syrup • Submersibles

Know How to Take Notes

Drawing a Model is the strategy featured in Chapter 7 (see page 312). Encourage your student to draw any visual models (pictures, graphs, charts, etc.) that are used in the lesson. Your student could also include his/her own original visual models to help remember a difficult concept or example. Have your student explain what each model represents and how it does this. To be most beneficial, students need to be as accurate and detailed as possible when drawing a model.

Middle School Math, Course 1
Professional Development Book

CHAPTER 7 Continued

Name _____ Date _____

Parents as Partners
Use with Chapter 7.

Key Ideas Your student can demonstrate understanding of key concepts by working through the following exercises with you.

Lesson	Exercise
7.1	You spend $\frac{3}{4}$ hour each day practicing the piano. How many hours are spent practicing each week? each month (30 days)?
7.2	$\frac{7}{8}$ of the students from a school participated in the school's Winter Carnival. $\frac{2}{3}$ of the students who participated in the carnival won prizes. What fraction of the total number of students won prizes? Bonus: If there are 600 students in the school, how many students won prizes?
7.3	You attend school from 8:30 A.M. to 3:20 P.M. How many hours is this? Write your answer as a mixed number. Of those hours, you are in class $\frac{3}{4}$ of the time. How many hours are you in class?
7.4	Your cat weighs 4 kilograms. Your gerbil weighs $\frac{3}{10}$ kilogram. How many gerbils would it take to equal the weight of your cat?
7.5	Find the quotient. (a) $3\frac{3}{8} \div \frac{3}{4}$ (b) $\frac{7}{10} \div 4\frac{1}{5}$ (c) $6 \div 6\frac{2}{7}$ (d) $4\frac{5}{6} \div 4\frac{2}{9}$
7.6	Choose an appropriate customary unit to measure the item. (a) capacity of a glass of milk (b) weight of a lunch tray (with lunch on it) (c) capacity of a wading pool (d) weight of a light bulb
7.7	Change the measurement to the specified unit. (a) New curtains require $6\frac{1}{2}$ yards of material. How many feet is that? (b) The cafeteria needs 23 quarts of milk each day. How many gallons is that? (c) The laundry detergent box weighed 128 ounces. How many pounds is that?

Home Involvement Activity

Directions: Use a map to find out how many miles you live from Winnipeg, Canada. Then change the measurement to yards, feet, and inches. Measure how tall you are in inches. Then change to feet and yards.

Answers

7.1: $5\frac{1}{4}$ hours; $22\frac{1}{2}$ hours 7.2: $\frac{7}{12}$; 350 students won prizes. 7.3: $6\frac{5}{6}$ hours in school; $5\frac{1}{8}$ hours in class 7.4: $13\frac{1}{3}$ or about 13 gerbils 7.5: (a) $4\frac{1}{2}$ (b) $\frac{1}{6}$ (c) $\frac{21}{22}$ (d) $1\frac{11}{76}$ 7.6: (a) fluid ounces or cups (b) pounds (c) gallons (d) ounces 7.7: (a) $19\frac{1}{2}$ feet (b) $5\frac{3}{4}$ gallons (c) 8 pounds

76 Middle School Math, Course 1
Professional Development Book

Chapter 7

Bulletin Board Idea

Use with Chapter 7.

Objective

To use the context and information from the Unit 2 poster to apply fraction concepts, represent fractional values graphically, and model fraction multiplication

Materials

- 3 sentence strips
- colored tape
- Unit 2 poster: On Parade
- 1 sheet of construction paper, 12 in. by 18 in.

Constructing the Bulletin Board

1. On the first sentence strip write the title of the bulletin board, "Fraction Formations." On the second strip write the title of the rectangular graph, "The Marching Band." On the third strip, write, "What fraction of the rectangle represents all the wind instruments?"

2. Position the title strip at the top of the bulletin board. Put the poster to the left, below the title. Place the graph title to the right of the poster.

3. Below the graph title, use the colored tape to make a frame with inside dimensions of 12 inches by 18 inches. Place the large piece of construction paper inside the frame.

Using the Bulletin Board

After students complete Lesson 7.2, discuss the bulletin board and its question with the class. You may want to include the following in the discussion.

- Ask students to identify what part of the band is comprised of wind instruments and what part of the wind instruments is comprised of woodwinds if $\frac{3}{5}$ of the wind instruments are brass instruments.

- Tell the class that the large sheet of construction paper represents the whole band. Ask students how they could fold the paper to represent the part of the band that is comprised of wind instruments. Students should recognize that the paper should be folded in half.

- Ask how they could show $\frac{2}{5}$ of the wind instruments, which represents the woodwinds.

    Students may suggest dividing the half of the paper that represents woodwinds into 5 parts and shading 2 of those parts. Ask students what fraction of the rectangle is shaded.

- Challenge students to use the diagram created above to explain the algorithm for multiplying fractions.

Follow-up

- Have students create their own visual models for multiplying fractions. Allow students to select an application that interests them. For example, students might investigate what fractions of the student body play various sports or like certain popular bands.

Middle School Math, Course 1
Professional Development Book

CHAPTER 8

Math Behind the Math

Use with Chapter 8.

Lessons 8.1–8.2

RATIOS Ratios and fractions are closely related. Fractions, which compare a part to a whole using division, are one type of ratio. Ratios, however, can also be of two other types. They can be part/part comparisons, or they can be whole/whole comparisons. For Example 1 of Lesson 8.1, the violas are $\frac{8}{35}$ of the whole orchestra. This ratio is a fraction. For Example 2, however, the double basses are not part of the cellos—they are a separate section entirely. This comparison is between two parts of the orchestra. It forms a part/part ratio, but not a fraction. Because the denominator of a fraction always gives the number of parts in the whole, and in a ratio, the second term may or may not give the number of parts in a whole, a fraction and a ratio are different.

Ratios and fractions differ in other ways, too. When talking about measurement, a fraction always compares two numbers with the same units, such as 6 miles to 12 miles. A ratio may not. It may compare 3 miles to 2 hours. Two ratios are never added or subtracted either, unlike fractions. If two teams have win/loss records of $\frac{5}{9}$ and $\frac{8}{9}$, the sum of $\frac{13}{9}$ (as computed for fractions) is meaningless in this context.

COMPARING RATIOS Students can compare ratios by writing them in fraction form or decimal form. Ratios are equivalent when the fractions or decimals that express them are equivalent. To determine if the ratios 2 : 5 and 8 : 20 are equivalent, you can write them as $\frac{2}{5}$ and $\frac{8}{20}$. Simplifying the second fraction shows that the ratios are equivalent. To compare ratios using decimals, rewrite the fractions as decimals. For example, both $\frac{2}{5}$ and $\frac{8}{20}$ are equal to 0.4. Because they have the same decimal value, they express the same ratio. The decimal form of ratios will become increasingly important to students when they begin working with ratios, such as π (about 3.14159) or the golden ratio (about 1.68), which cannot be expressed as fractions.

RATES Ratios expressing the change of one measured quantity to another are called *rates*. The usual way to express a rate is as a *unit rate*. A unit rate is expressed as some amount of one quantity per unit of the other. Some examples might include miles per gallon (mi/gal), kilometers per hour (km/h), kilograms of fish eaten per person per year, or the cost of a bulk food purchase per ounce. Unit rates express how long, how much, or how many of one quantity produces one unit of another quantity. Often a rate reports an *average*. For example, when a car travels 255 km in 3 hours, it is said to have traveled at a rate of 85 km/h. While the car did not travel *exactly* 85 km/h for the entire 3-hour trip, it did in the end cover 255 km in 3 hours. Thus, a rate reports the car's average speed throughout the trip.

Lesson 8.3

PROPORTIONS Throughout history "good proportions" expressed within creations, such as buildings, have been valued. Ancient architects followed mathematical ratios and proportions that they observed within nature to create beauty and unity within buildings. Proportions and ratios often are used interchangeably, but they are not the same. Mathematically, a *proportion* sets forth *two* ratios that are equal to each other.

SOLUTION OF A PROPORTION One of the most frequent mathematical tasks students will face in life is the need to *solve a proportion*. In these cases, the ratio representing one side of the proportion is known, but a quantity within the ratio on the other side is missing.

The methods for solving proportions become more complex and appropriate to larger sets of numbers as the chapter progresses. In Lesson 8.1 students use the method of equivalent fractions to solve proportions. This is a technique they have used for several years, but is usually used only when one fraction is a whole number multiple of the other.

78 Middle School Math, Course 1
Professional Development Book

Math Behind the Math

Use with Chapter 8.

The method of Lesson 8.2 is an extension of the equivalent fraction method, but is useful even when the terms of the proportion contain fractions and decimals, as long as the denominator of one ratio is 1. The method of solving proportions by using cross products is the most general method possible. Once students can solve proportions using this method they can solve any proportion, no matter what type of numbers are used in the two ratios. In Grade 6, the expanding nature of the possible solutions may not be evident to students, since most exercises still retain whole number solutions. But the reason students learn all three methods is so that they can solve the whole range of possible proportions.

Lesson 8.4

SCALE DRAWINGS A *scale drawing* is a drawing that represents a real object. The *scale* is the size of a represented object relative to its actual size. A scale can be represented by either a ratio or a rate. The relative size of the model and the real object can be expressed either using the same units, such as 1 : 48, or different units, such as 1 inch : 4 feet. Notice that both these scales would represent a model of the same size, because 48 inches = 4 feet.

Blueprints and maps are common examples of scale drawings. But models are so common in real life that we take most of the examples for granted. Other models students may be familiar with include models of the solar system and of atomic structures in science, models of teeth and eyes in doctors' offices, and models of railroad stock, airplanes, and doll houses for hobbyists.

In a blueprint or map, a scale is the ratio of 1 unit to a number of another units, such as 1 cm : 10 km or 1 cm : 100 km. The larger that the second measurement is, the smaller the features of the map or a scale drawing will appear to be.

Lessons 8.5–8.7

PERCENT The word *percent* means "out of one hundred." Percents are used to describe a portion of a whole that has been divided into 100 parts. Any ratio can be expressed as a percent. Often, when a set of ratios have different second terms (or denominators), the ratios are written as percents for ease of comparison. Writing these ratios as a percent is similar to writing them as fractions with a denominator of 100. Percents, in effect, write all ratios with a common second term (or denominator).

Percents are not the only way to write ratios with a common second term. For example, in ecology, ratios are often expressed in units called ppm and ppb, parts per million and parts per billion. Real estate tax rates are expressed as dollars per thousand dollars. For most practical purposed, however, percents are used.

EQUIVALENT VALUES Students can easily write a percent as a decimal by moving the decimal point two places to the left. Remind them to also remove the percent sign. Any percent can also be written as a fraction by placing it over 100. Students should recognize *equivalent values* in many real-life situations, such as knowing that a "$\frac{1}{2}$ off sale" and a "50% off sale" mean the same thing.

GROWTH OF A QUANTITY Percents are often used to present growth of a quantity. *Interest* paid in finance is a good example of how growth can be expressed as a percent. In the lesson, students are asked to use the simple interest formula that gives fixed interest for one time period. In future math courses, students will be exposed to more sophisticated interest formulas, such as compound interest.

CHAPTER 8: Tips for New Teachers

Use with Chapter 8.

Lesson 8.1

INCLUSION To help visual learners understand ratios, have each student draw and shade the circles shown below. Next, ask students to write part-part and part-to-whole ratios for each circle. Then have them compare the number of parts in the two circles by writing whole-to-whole ratios.

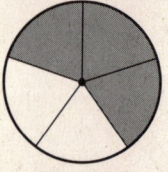

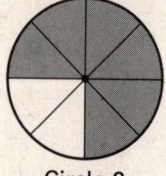

Circle 1   Circle 2

TEACHING TIP When ratios are written as decimals, as in Example 3, the dividend and divisor are no longer evident, as they are in other forms of a ratio. Remind students that a decimal such as 0.6 can be thought of as the ratio "6 out of 10."

Lesson 8.2

TEACHING TIP List on the board any rates that students are familiar with, such as miles per hour, miles per gallon, and population per square mile. Then post this list in the classroom and have students add to it as they complete this chapter. Seeing the many contexts in which rates are used is an effective motivational device.

TEACHING TIP Bring a grocery store ad to class and use it as an additional example of a unit rate. Let students choose the unit rates they will calculate. They will find some easy to do, such as 2 boxes for $3, 5 containers for $4, and so on. Other unit rates may be difficult and a little beyond the computational skills of some students, for example, finding the unit rate for an ounce of cheese that is 7.5 ounces for $1.29. Record these more difficult-to-calculate rates in a place where you can return to them in a few days. Tell students that in the next few days they will learn how to calculate these unit rates as well.

Lesson 8.3

TEACHING TIP Students may wonder why they need to learn a second method for finding equal ratios because they already know that they can find them just as they did using equivalent fractions. You may want to suggest the following problem.

You are reading a book that has 388 pages. It has taken you $2\frac{1}{2}$ hours to read the first 124 pages. If you continue reading at the same rate, how long will it take you to read the whole book?

Solving this problem using equivalent fractions is difficult. Solving the proportion using cross products, however, is a straightforward process.

TEACHING TIP Using cross products to solve proportions is very abstract to some students. To help them understand why a cross product works, have them consider two equivalent fractions such as $\frac{2}{3}$ and $\frac{8}{12}$. Write the second the numerator and denominator of the second fraction in their factored forms and see what the cross product now looks like.

$$\frac{2}{3} = \frac{2}{3}$$

$$\frac{2}{3} = \frac{2 \times 4}{3 \times 4}$$

Then the cross products of this equation are 2 · 3 · 4 and 3 · 2 · 4. Both cross products contain as factors the numerator and denominator of the original fraction, 2 and 3, and the factor that the numerator and denominator were increased by, 4. Because the two cross products contain exactly the same factors, they are equal.

Lesson 8.4

COMMON ERROR Order is extremely important when writing ratios and proportions. Some students may not write the terms of a proportion in the correct order. When you have students write proportions, ask them to include the units—foot, inch, pound, dollars, etc. Doing this helps insure that the same units are used in first and third terms of the proportion. This will correct many of the problems in writing proportions.

Middle School Math, Course 1
Professional Development Book

CHAPTER 8 Continued

Tips for New Teachers
Use with Chapter 8.

INCLUSION To help your visual learners see why the result of Example 3 is true, have students draw a rectangle that is 2 units by 3 units on graph paper. Then have them draw rectangles that have dimensions 2, 3, and 4 times those of the first rectangle. Have students subdivide each of the larger rectangles into rectangles that are the size of the original. This will help students see how the original fits into the larger rectangles 4, 9, and 16 times. The application of this result will surprise many students. To make an enlargement of a photo that doubles the length and width, you need four times as much paper.

Lesson 8.5

TEACHING TIP When students wonder why they need to learn about percents (when they already have fractions and decimals to represent parts of a whole), show them the following example.

Keisha scored 25 out of 32 points on one test and 39 out of 48 points on another. On which test did she score better?

She can compare her scores as fractions $\left(\frac{25}{32} \text{ and } \frac{39}{48}\right)$ or as percents (78% and 81%). Percents are easier to use here, and in many other cases, because percents are one way of writing fractions with a common denominator, a denominator of 100.

TEACHING TIP Bring to class a circle graph from a newspaper or magazine. Be sure each section is labeled in percents. Use this "real" data to make up additional examples of circle graphs. If the sum of the percents does not total 100%, discuss with students the rounding errors that may have accumulated.

Lesson 8.6

INCLUSION Students are most familiar with simple fractions in which the numerator and the denominator are integers. Lesson 8.5 introduced a few complex fractions such as $\frac{2.5}{100}$ to students. Use Example 2c as an opportunity to review complex fractions. Take a few minutes to make your reluctant student comfortable with the complex fraction $\frac{2.5}{100}$. Model the fraction on a decimal square, shading 2.5 squares. List for students the decimal, percent, and fraction equivalents and have them explain how to move from one form to another. Then have students list the equivalents for $\frac{7.5}{100}$ (0.075, 7.5%, and $\frac{75}{1000}$) and $\frac{11.5}{100}$ (0.115, 11.5%, and $\frac{23}{2000}$). The ability to change these complex fractions from one form to another will give students a starting point for attacking problems that use numbers such as these.

TEACHING TIP Encourage students to memorize the table of common percents shown on page 401. This information will be especially useful to students on standardized tests because it will allow them to do many simple conversion problems using mental math. Having saved time on simpler problems, students will then be able to spend more time on difficult problems. These equivalent relationships are also useful when students check homework problems for reasonableness and make estimates in many real-life situations. You may also want to suggest that students include the decimal and percent equivalents for $\frac{1}{6}$ (0.1$\overline{6}$, about 17%), $\frac{1}{8}$ (0.125, 12.5%), and $\frac{1}{10}$ (0.1, 10%) to this list.

Lesson 8.7

TEACHING TIP For Example 2, you may want to show students how to find the sale price with just one calculation. Because 10% of the price is being discounted, the current price is 90% of the original price. So, the sale price is 90% of $40, or $36.

TEACHING TIP Teach students how to calculate a tip mentally. For example, to estimate a 15% tip on a $17.53 bill, students can use these steps:

- Round the price of the meal to the nearest dollar. ($17.53 rounds to $18.)

- Find 10% of $18 mentally and round to the nearest $.50. (10% of $18 is $1.80. Round $1.80 to $2.)

- Find 5% of $18. This is half of the 10%. (Half of $2 is $1.)

- Combine the two percentages to find 15%. ($2 + $1 = $3. The tip is about $3.)

Middle School Math, Course 1
Professional Development Book

CHAPTER 8

Name _____ Date _____

Parents as Partners

Use with Chapter 8.

Chapter Overview One way you can help your student succeed in Chapter 8 is by discussing the lesson goals in the chart below. When a lesson is completed, ask your student the following questions. "What were the goals of the lesson? What new words and formulas did you learn? How can you apply the ideas of the lesson to your life?"

Lesson Title	Lesson Goals	Key Applications
8.1: Ratios	Write ratios and equivalent ratios. Compare ratios using decimals.	• School Orchestras • Football • Average Temperatures • Baseball
8.2: Rates	Write rates, equivalent rates, and unit rates. Compare unit rates.	• Space • Movies • Hummingbirds • Niagara Falls
8.3: Solving Proportions	Write and solve proportions.	• Boating • Literature • Currency
8.4: Proportions and Scale Drawings	Use proportions to find measures of objects.	• Soap Box Derby • School Mural • Landscape Architects
8.5: Understanding Percent	Write percents as decimals and fractions. Use circle graphs with percents.	• Dog Survey • Exercise • Computer Use
8.6: Percents, Decimals, and Fractions	Write fractions and decimals as percents. Use common relationships between percents, decimals, and fractions.	• Volleyball • Field Trip • Sewing • Deserts
8.7: Finding a Percent of a Number	Multiply to find a percent of a number. Find a discount. Find sales tax. Find simple interest.	• Sneaker Sale • Feeding Your Dog • Savings • Clothing

Know How to Take Notes

Drawing a Concept Map is the strategy featured in Chapter 8 (see page 372). By connecting the ideas this way *on paper*, your student is also organizing the ideas and relationships *mentally*. Your student will be more likely to remember the concepts and how they relate. Check to see that your student has added the category of percents to the concept map from page 372. See if your student can clearly explain the relationships depicted by the map.

Chapter 8 Continued

Name _____ Date _____

Parents as Partners
Use with Chapter 8.

Key Ideas Your student can demonstrate understanding of key concepts by working through the following exercises with you.

Lesson	Exercise
8.1	During the month of April, it rained 18 days. Write the ratio of days it rained to days in April in simplest form in three different ways. Write the ratio of days it did *not* rain to days in April in simplest form. (There are 30 days in April.)
8.2	You can purchase a package of 12 pencils for $3.75 or a package of 3 pencils for $1. Which is the better buy? Why?
8.3	The value of 102 Taiwan dollars is about 3 U.S. dollars. What is the value of 25 U.S. dollars in Taiwan dollars?
8.4	A model of the old Pittsburgh baseball field, Forbes Field, uses the scale 1 in.: 48 ft. The right foul line of the model measures 6.25 inches. What was the actual length of the right foul line?
8.5	There were 100 questions on a test. You got 84 questions correct. Write this result as a percent, a decimal, and a fraction.
8.6	You must start in 85% of your basketball games to be eligible for the all-star team. So far, you have started in 14 of the 16 games. Are you eligible? Bonus: If there are 2 more games in the season, how many more games do you need to start in to be eligible for the all-star team? Why?
8.7	Find the cost described. (a) The price of a pair of shoes is $42.60. Find the cost with a sales tax of 5%. (b) A video's regular price is $18.50. Find the cost after a 10% discount. (c) The price of a meal is $24.80. Find the cost with a 15% tip.

Home Involvement Activity

Directions: Use the simple interest formula to make a chart that compares the amounts of money you can earn over a 5-year period using different annual interest rates. Be sure to use the same principal amount. What patterns do you notice?

Answers
8.1: ratio for days rained: $\frac{3}{5}$, 3 : 5, 3 to 5; ratio for days it didn't rain: $\frac{2}{5}$. **8.2:** package of 12 pencils; unit prices: $.31 < $.33. **8.3:** 850 Taiwan dollars. **8.4:** 300 feet. **8.5:** 84%, 0.84, $\frac{21}{25}$. **8.6:** yes, 87.5% > 85%; Both games; Starting in 16 games is over 88%, but starting in 15 games is only 83%. **8.7:** (a) The total cost is $44.73. (b) The total cost is $16.65. (c) The total cost is $28.52.

CHAPTER 8

Bulletin Board Idea

Use with Chapter 8.

Objective

To visually reinforce the concepts of scale and proportion.

Materials

- maps of area or state that use different scales
- 8 sentence strips
- map pins or colored pushpins
- yarn or string

Constructing the Bulletin Board

1. On the bulletin board, display at least two maps that have different scales. The scales should be clearly visible. On each map, place a length of yarn between each of three pairs of towns or landmarks that are familiar to students. Use pushpins to attach the ends of the yarn lengths to the map.

2. On the first six sentence strips, write the names of the towns or landmarks that you have attached yarn to. Place these strips beside the map and use yarn to run a pointer from each pair of towns to its sentence strip.

3. On one sentence strip, write the title of the bulletin board, "How Far Apart Are These Places?" On another sentence strip, ask, "What is the ratio of measured distance to real distance for each map scale?" Post this strip near one of the map scales.

Using the Bulletin Board

After students complete Lesson 6.4, discuss the bulletin board and its questions with the class. Explain to students that they can determine the actual distance between two points on a map using the map scale. The discussion and the solution to the problem may include the following points.

- A large area can be represented by a smaller area when using a scale drawing. The ratio of the measured distance to the actual distance it represents is called the *scale* of the map. For instance, if 2.5 miles is represented by 1 inch on the map, then the scale of that map is 1 in. : 2.5 mi.

- To calculate the actual distance or measurement from a scale drawing, write a proportion using the scale of the drawing as the first ratio, and the measured distance to actual distance (unknown) as the second ratio. Solve for the unknown.

Follow-up

- Have students create a scale drawing of the classroom using graph paper. You may provide students with relevant measurements, or have them take their own measurements of the classroom, working in teams.

84 Middle School Math, Course 1
Professional Development Book

CHAPTER 9

Math Behind the Math

Use with Chapter 9.

Lesson 9.1

EUCLIDIAN GEOMETRY Many of the ideas for what is considered "a course of basic geometry" today were laid out in the *The Elements* of Euclid, written about 300 B.C. Euclid set forth several postulates, one being that a straight line is defined by two points. He also developed methods to prove propositions about points and lines, using a compass and a straightedge. So, the geometry that most students study is actually more than 2000 years old.

Lessons 9.2–9.3

MEASURING ANGLES Circles and angles are closely related to each other. In the *degree* system of angle measures, an angle measure of one complete revolution is equal to 360°. An advantage of this system is that it gives easy-to-remember degree measures for common angles. Notice that 360 is divisible by 1, 2, 3, 4, 5, 6, 8, 9, 10, 12, 15, 18, 20, 24, 30, 36, 40, 45, 60, 72, 90, 120, 180, and 360. Many of these divisors of 360 represent angles that are often used. For example, a half revolution, or *straight angle*, is 180°; a quarter revolution, or *right angle* is 90°; half of a right angle is 45°; and so on. So, most calculations within the 360° system are simple.

Students should know that while the 360° system is common and will be used for ordinary work where angle measurements are required, mathematicians, scientists, and engineers do have other systems for measuring angles. The most important of these is the *radian* system of angle measure. Most scientific calculators can use either degrees or radians where angles are concerned, so students should learn how these two systems differ.

To understand where radians come from, it is important to think about the relationship between angle measurements and distance traveled around an arc of a circle. Recall that the distance around a circle is about three times the length of its diameter. Referring to Lesson 10.3, $2\pi r$ is equal to the circumference of the circle, where r is the radius of the circle. If radians are used to measure angles, then an angle of 2π radians is a full circle. So, 2π radians (approximately 6.28 radians) is equal to

360°. If an angle in radians is multiplied by the radius, the result is equal to the distance around the part of the circular path, or *arc length*, at that radius. For this reason, radians are considered a natural way to measure angles.

Below are a few sample angles followed by a table that gives their descriptions and measures.

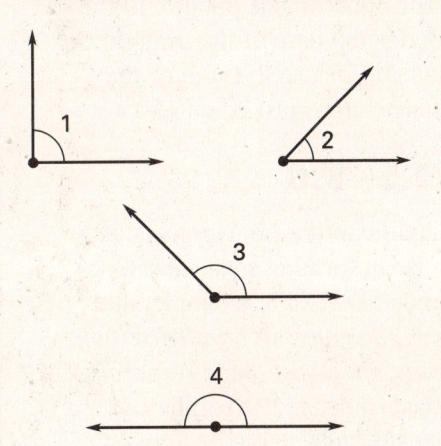

Angle Number	Type of Angle	Measure in Degrees	Measure in Radians
1	right	90°	$\dfrac{\pi}{2}$
2	acute	45°	$\dfrac{\pi}{4}$
3	obtuse	135°	$\dfrac{3\pi}{4}$
4	straight	180°	π

Lesson 9.4

ANGLES OF A TRIANGLE The sum of the interior angles of any triangle is always 180°. The reason this is true is shown in a proof provided by *The Elements* of Euclid. The diagram below illustrates this reasoning.

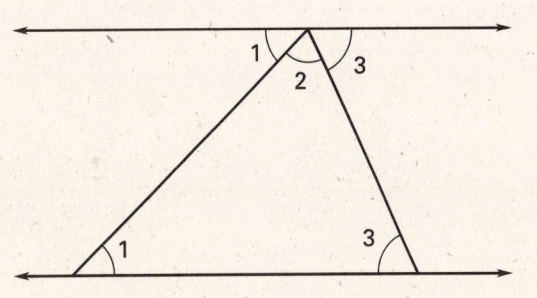

Math Behind the Math

Use with Chapter 9.

In *The Elements*, it is postulated that the opposite interior angles are equal when a line is drawn to intersect a pair of parallel lines. In the diagram, on page 85, two such lines intersect parallel lines. Notice how the two lines intersect to create a triangle. Angles *1*, *2*, and *3* that form the triangle also combine to exactly span a straight angle along the upper line. The upper line is parallel to the lower line that forms the base of the triangle. A straight angle equals 180°, so the sum of the angles of the triangle also must equal 180°.

Lessons 9.5–9.6

POLYGONS Classification of polygons is an interesting exercise in forming sets, subsets, and the intersection of sets. For example, all *quadrilaterals* are *polygons*; all *parallelograms*, *rectangles*, *squares*, *rhombuses*, and *trapezoids* are quadrilaterals; trapezoids are not parallelograms; squares are rectangles; and so on.

DIAGONALS There is a simple formula for determining the number, *n*, of all possible *diagonals* in any *convex* polygon:

$$n = \frac{s(s-3)}{2}$$

where *s* is the number of sides.

Lesson 9.7

CONGRUENCE AND SIMILARITY *Congruence* is a strong condition that includes *similarity*. For two polygons to be congruent, they must be identical in every aspect — the number of sides must be the same for each polygon, the lengths of *corresponding sides* must be congruent, and all corresponding interior angles must be congruent. For two polygons to be similar, only their corresponding interior angles need to be congruent.

Lesson 9.8

USES OF SYMMETRY When mathematicians began studying *symmetries* in sets, known as *groups*, about 200 years ago, no one knew how important symmetry would become to physical science today. An interesting application involves the way atoms and molecules behave in crystal structures, such as in the materials that are used to make computer chips. Mathematicians and scientists begin to look at symmetries in these materials by considering the properties of the polygons that students study in this lesson.

TILING PATTERNS Investigating tiling patterns on a flat surface is fun for many students. Polygons with 3-fold symmetry (equilateral triangles), 4-fold symmetry (squares), or 6-fold symmetry (regular hexagons) will cover a plane. However, regular pentagons with 5-fold symmetry cannot by themselves cover a plane without leaving all sorts of unsightly gaps.

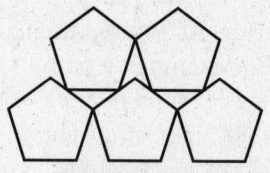

Does not cover

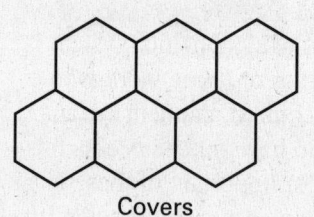

Covers

Allow students to experiment with creating different tiling combinations using pattern tiles. Although these are only the ways to tessellate or cover a plane using a single type of regular polygons, the number of other ways is infinite. If you allow 2 or 3 types of regular polygons to be used, 8 semi-regular patterns can be found. The works of M.L. Escher shows some of the other infinite possibilities that use non-regular figures.

Chapter 9: Tips for New Teachers
Use with Chapter 9.

Lesson 9.1

COMMON ERROR Some students will name a ray, such as the one below, $\vec{BA}$ instead of $\vec{AB}$. Remind students that the first letter in the name of a ray is its vertex.

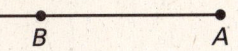

←————•————————•
      B   A

TEACHING TIP Have students notice that in the diagram above Example 3, the first plane has no dot to show where point *P* is located. When this happens, as in Example 3, the point is assumed to be the point of intersection.

Lesson 9.2

COMMON ERROR Some students may not have used a protractor before to measure angles. One thing to watch for is students who read the wrong scale of a protractor with a double scale. Remind students that when they place the protractor atop a ray at 0, the scale with the 0 is the scale they should read. If you encourage students to count up—0, 10, 20, . . .—they will learn to look for this starting point on the scale.

Some students may also have a problem measuring adjacent angles. These students will place the 0 mark on a ray that is not part of the correct angle. Suggest that students highlight the angle they are measuring when there are overlapping angles involved. Sometimes it helps students measure angles in the text book by tracing the angles and extending their rays, in effect, making larger images of the angles.

TEACHING TIP Before asking students to estimate the measures of the angles in Example 3, have students name all ten angles that are in the diagram. Some students may have a problem seeing the overlapping angles, such as ∠EDF, ∠BDF, and ∠EDC. You may also want to have students measure some of the angles that have no horizontal rays. Because some students may not have tried this before, it might be confusing to them.

Lesson 9.3

TEACHING TIP Be sure students note the red right angle mark at ∠A in the diagram in Example 1. They should understand that it represents information about the figure, namely that ∠A is a right angle.

COMMON ERROR Some students may confuse acute angles and obtuse angles. Have students look up the nonmathematical meanings of these words in the dictionary. They will find that *acute* means *sharp*, or *pointed*. The word *obtuse* means *dull*, or *blunt*. Therefore, an acute angle is a sharp angle and an obtuse angle is a blunt angle.

TEACHING TIP Many students recall that there are two types of angles, *complementary* and *supplementary*. They also recall that the sum of the angles for one is 90°, and the sum of the angles for the other is 180°. To help students match which measure relates to which term, have them write the two words down and look at the first few letters of each word. The word *complementary* begins with the letters "co," and in a sense, these letters look a little like the number "90." Since complementary angles have a sum of 90°, the other word, *supplementary*, relates to "180°".

Lesson 9.4

COMMON ERROR Some students may not recognize which points constitute a triangle. Be sure students understand that a triangle consists only of the line segments that form it. The points of the plane within the triangle make up its interior and are not part of the triangle itself.

TEACHING TIP In discussing acute, right, and obtuse triangles, ask students if they can draw a triangle that has two right angles. Students should see that if two right angles are placed on either end of one horizontal side of a triangle, then the two vertical rays of these angles can never meet. No triangle will be formed. The same is true when trying to construct a triangle with two obtuse angles.

Tips for New Teachers

Use with Chapter 9.

TEACHING TIP Present to students the skeleton of the table below. Have student pairs explore how to draw a triangle with both attributes noted in the diagram. For example, have students find if it is possible to draw an acute scalene triangle. After students have experimented for a while, help them understand that no equilateral triangle can have a right angle or an obtuse angle.

	Acute	Right	Obtuse
Scalene	△	△	△
Isosceles	△	△	△
Equilateral	△	Not Possible	Not Possible

Lesson 9.5

COMMON ERROR Even after classifying many quadrilaterals, some students will have difficulty classifying a diamond shape, because rhombuses are usually shown with one horizontal side. Have students check opposite sides for parallelism and compare the lengths of the four sides. From these measures they should be able to conclude that a diamond-shaped figure is a rhombus.

TEACHING TIP Have students explore the greatest number of obtuse angles that a quadrilateral can have. Students can easily find that a quadrilateral can have two obtuse angles when it is a parallelogram. If students are challenged searching for three obtuse angles, help them create a kite-shaped quadrilateral with three obtuse angles of 100° and one 60° angle.

Lesson 9.6

TEACHING TIP The student text shows several examples of polygons, but you may also want to share with students some figures that come close to being polygons but do not fit all the requirements.

Other figures that would not be polygons include the following.

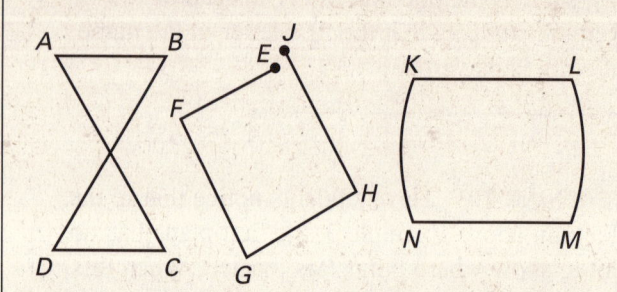

COMMON ERROR Some students may think that every diagonal contains the center of a polygon, as it does in parallelograms, rectangles, and squares. When discussing Example 3, you may want to point out that none of the diagonals of a regular pentagon contain its center. You may want students to explore the diagonals of a regular hexagon also. Only one third of its diagonals contain its center.

Lesson 9.7

COMMON ERROR Some students may think that any two parallelograms are similar because they have the same shape. Explain that what is meant by *the same shape* is that the figures are an enlargement or reduction of each other.

COMMON ERROR Some students may not understand how much information is in the statement "△ABC is *congruent* to △JKL." Not only does this mean that the two triangles are congruent, but that point A corresponds to point J, that point B corresponds to point K, and that point C corresponds to point L.

Lesson 9.8

INCLUSION For your visual students, try a change of pace after Example 3. Have each student create a symmetric design with directions on how to draw it that another student can follow. Students should draw the design on dot paper, making sure it has at least one line of symmetry.

CHAPTER 9

Name _____ **Date** _____

Parents as Partners

Use with Chapter 9.

Chapter Overview One way you can help your student succeed in Chapter 9 is by discussing the lesson goals in the chart below. When a lesson is completed, ask your student the following questions. "What were the goals of the lesson? What new words and formulas did you learn? How can you apply the ideas of the lesson to your life?"

Lesson Title	Lesson Goals	Key Applications
9.1: Introduction to Geometry	Identify lines, rays, and segments. Identify intersecting and parallel lines.	• Aerial Photo • Swimming Pool • City Map
9.2: Angles	Name, measure, and draw angles. Estimate angle measures.	• Miniature Golf • Kite Flying
9.3: Classifying Angles	Classify angles and find angle measures.	• Scissors • Tower of Pisa • Clock Hands • Mirrors
9.4: Classifying Triangles	Classify triangles by their angles and by their sides. Find angle measures of triangles.	• Stamps • Flags • Great Pyramid
9.5: Classifying Quadrilaterals	Classify quadrilaterals by their angles and sides. Draw a quadrilateral.	• Quilts • Woodworking
9.6: Polygons	Classify polygons by their sides. Find diagonals of a polygon.	• Soccer • Stained Glass Windows
9.7: Congruent and Similar Figures	Identify similar and congruent figures. List and use corresponding parts.	• Bridges • Photography • Shirt Buttons • Batteries
9.8: Line Symmetry	Identify lines of symmetry. Complete a drawing of a symmetrical figure.	• Paper Folding • Tennis Court

Know How to Take Notes

Drawing a Venn Diagram is the strategy featured in Chapter 9 (see page 420). Have your student draw a Venn Diagram to show the relationships about quadrilaterals presented in Lesson 9.5. Ask your student to explain the relationships illustrated in the diagram. Do the regions overlap correctly?

Middle School Math, Course 1
Professional Development Book

CHAPTER 9 Continued

Name _____ **Date** _____

Parents as Partners
Use with Chapter 9.

Key Ideas Your student can demonstrate understanding of key concepts by working through the following exercises with you.

Lesson	Exercise
9.1	Use the figure to the right. (a) Name 2 points. (b) Name 2 rays. (c) Name 2 intersecting lines. (d) Which lines are parallel?
9.2	Use the figure from Lesson 9.1 to locate and name an angle whose measure is close to the given measure. (a) 90° (b) 135° (c) 45°
9.3	Use the figure from Lesson 9.1 to name the following pairs of angles of each type that share vertex C. (a) vertical (b) supplementary
9.4	Name six types of triangles and write the defining characteristic for each type.
9.5	Suppose you have a rhombus. What would have to be special about the rhombus for it to be a rectangle? Would it need anything else special to be a square? Explain.
9.6	Sketch a pentagon. Draw a diagonal. Classify the two polygons formed from the diagonal and sides of the pentagon.
9.7	△ MNP and △ RST are similar. List the corresponding parts.
9.8	Divide the capital letters of the alphabet into 3 groups according to their having 0, 1, or 2 or more lines of symmetry.

Home Involvement Activity

Directions: You have probably noticed many objects with geometric patterns in or on them such as floor tiles, wallpaper prints, and stained glass windows. Create your own patterned design on paper using only regular polygons. (*Hint:* Use only 2 or 3 different polygons. Make patterns for each polygon to use for tracing congruent polygons on your paper.)

Answers

9.1: *Sample Answers:* (a) A, D (b) $\overrightarrow{EF}$ and $\overrightarrow{BD}$ (c) $\overleftrightarrow{EA}$ and $\overleftrightarrow{FA}$ (d) $\overleftrightarrow{BC}$ and $\overleftrightarrow{EF}$ **9.2:** *Sample Answers:* (a) ∠EAF (b) ∠ACD (c) ∠BEF **9.3:** (a) ∠ACB and ∠DCF; ∠ACD and ∠BCF (b) ∠ACD and ∠DCF; ∠ACB and ∠BCF **9.4:** *acute:* 3 acute angles; *obtuse:* 1 obtuse angle; *right:* 1 right angle; *equilateral:* 3 equal sides; *isosceles:* at least 2 equal sides; *scalene:* 3 sides with different lengths. **9.5:** A rhombus is a parallelogram. If it also has 4 right angles, then it is a rectangle. If it is a square because a rhombus has 4 equal sides. **9.6:** Sketches will vary; triangle, quadrilateral. **9.7:** ∠M and ∠R, ∠N and ∠S, ∠P and ∠T; $\overline{MN}$ and $\overline{RS}$, $\overline{NP}$ and $\overline{ST}$, $\overline{PM}$ and $\overline{TR}$ **9.8:** 0 lines: F, G, J, K, L, N, P, Q, R, S, Z; 1 line: A–E, M, T–W, Y; 2 or more lines: H, I, O, X

90 **Middle School Math, Course 1**
Professional Development Book

Copyright © McDougal Littell Inc.
All rights reserved.

Bulletin Board Idea

Use with Chapter 9.

Objective

To use the context from the Unit 3 poster to identify line and point symmetry and to investigate symmetry of congruent and similar figures.

Materials

- a 4 in. by 4 in. square of paper
- sentence strips
- black yarn
- an enlarged photocopy of square
- Unit 3 poster: Designs on Display

Constructing the Bulletin Board

1. Draw a design with line symmetry on the square of paper. Enlarge this design using a photocopier and colored paper.

2. Write out two sentence strips. The first is the title of the bulletin board, "Designs on Display." The second strip should read "How many lines of symmetry?"

3. Position the title strip at the top of the bulletin board. Put the poster to the left, below the title. Place the second strip at the top of the space to the right of the poster. Beneath this strip, position the two squares with the similar figures.

4. Using pieces of black yarn, indicate the lines of symmetry on the larger figure.

Using the Bulletin Board

After students complete Lesson 9.7, discuss the bulletin board and its question with the class. You may wish to include the following points.

- The yarn indicates the lines of symmetry on the larger figure. Ask students to use yarn to identify the lines of symmetry on the smaller figure.

- Ask students to submit their own drawings of similar and congruent figures for use on other days. Change the design a couple of times each week.

- With each design, invite students to use the yarn to show lines of symmetry. Ask questions such as, "Do the two figures have the same number of lines of symmetry?" and "Are the lines of symmetry in the same position on both figures?"

- After students have investigated these questions using several designs, ask, "Do two similar (or congruent) figures always have the same number of lines of symmetry? In congruent and similar figures, will lines of symmetry always be in the same positions?" Challenge students to draw similar (or congruent) figures that do not have the same lines of symmetry.

- After students have completed the worksheet on the back of the poster, ask them if point symmetry is also the same on similar and congruent figures.

Follow-up

- Invite students to submit drawings of their own symmetric designs and post them around the classroom.

Middle School Math, Course 1
Professional Development Book

CHAPTER 10

Math Behind the Math

Use with Chapter 10.

Lesson 10.1

AREA OF A PARALLELOGRAM The concept of area is extended in this lesson to figures other than rectangles. The area of a parallelogram is equal to the length of one side called its *base*, b, multiplied by its *height*, h. The height is the distance to the opposite side along a perpendicular line drawn from the base. So, the formula for the *area*, A, of a parallelogram is $A = bh$.

It is easy to see why this is the correct formula, because the parallelogram can be transformed into a rectangle of equal area. This is accomplished by cutting a right triangle from one end of it and sliding it to fit on the opposite end, thus forming a rectangle. The area covered by the rectangle with sides of length h and b, $A = bh$ is the same as that of the original parallelogram.

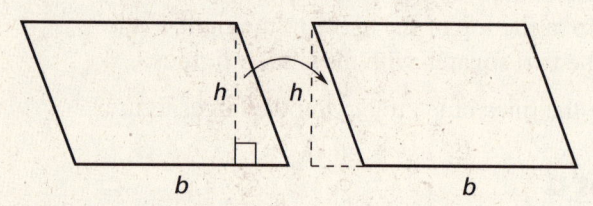

Lesson 10.2

AREA OF A TRIANGLE The formula for the area of a triangle follows directly from the formula for the area of a parallelogram. Note the shaded triangle in the figure shown below.

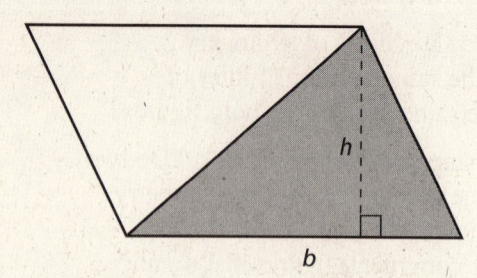

The triangle was formed by drawing a diagonal that splits the area of the parallelogram exactly in two. We already know that the area of the parallelogram is bh. The area, A, of the shaded part (the triangle with the same base and height as the whole parallelogram), would then be equal to exactly half the area of the whole parallelogram, or $A = \frac{1}{2}bh$.

It is important to realize that the choice of which side to use as the base is arbitrary. Any of the three sides of a triangle can be used. The height will always be measured along a perpendicular line from the chosen base to the opposite vertex. In some triangles and for certain choices of the base, the line along which the height is measured is actually outside the triangle. The length of the base is *not* to include this extended part. An example is shown below.

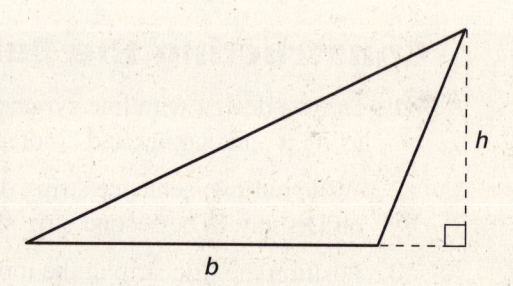

Lessons 10.3–10.4

Pi The Greek letter pi (π) is used to represent one of the most important numbers in all mathematics. It is the ratio of the circumference (the distance around) of any circle to the length of its diameter. So, $C = \pi d$, where C is the circumference and d is the diameter. Below is the value of π to 23 decimal places.

3.14159265358979323846264 . . .

The ratio represented by π is the same for all circles. It has been calculated to millions of decimal places using formulas from advance mathematics and aided by computer calculations.

Though use of the symbol π to represent this ratio dates from only the eighteenth century A.D., its numerical value was sought throughout the early history of mathematics. Archimedes of Syracuse (287–212 B.C.) obtained the approximation $\frac{223}{71} < \pi < \frac{22}{7}$.

Students should understand that π is *not* a rational number. It is an *irrational number*. Its digits do not repeat and do not form any pattern. There is no way to write the exact value of π as the ratio of integers. The values $\frac{22}{7}$ and 3.14 are just approximations of π. But these approximations will be used for most work.

Middle School Math, Course 1
Professional Development Book

CHAPTER 10 Continued

Math Behind the Math

Use with Chapter 10.

AREA OF A CIRCLE The calculation of the area enclosed by a circle was another problem of great interest to the mathematicians of antiquity. *The Elements* of Euclid (300 B.C.) contains proof that the ratio of the areas of two circles is equal to the ratio of the *squares* of their diameters.

The modern formula for the area enclosed by a circle is $A = \pi r^2$, where r is the radius of the circle. To see why this works, first recall the relationship between the circumference and the diameter of a circle, $C = \pi d = 2\pi r$. (The diameter is two times the radius.) Now imagine that the circle is covered by a very large number of identical triangles all meeting at the center of the circle.

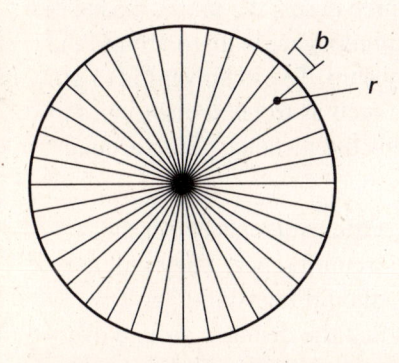

If the triangles are thin enough, then the radius of the circle becomes very close to the height of each triangle. The sum of the lengths of the bases of the little triangles becomes very close to the circumference of the circle, and the total area of all the triangles is very close to the area enclosed by the circle. The full calculation is shown below.

$$A = \frac{1}{2}br + \frac{1}{2}br + \cdots$$
$$= \frac{1}{2}(b + b + b + \cdots)r$$
$$= \frac{1}{2}Cr = \frac{1}{2} \times 2\pi r \times r = \pi r^2$$

Lesson 10.5

PROPERTIES OF POLYHEDRA Solids that have curved surfaces are distinguished from polyhedra—the solids that have all planar surfaces. Solids like spheres, cylinders, cones, ovoids (eggs), and toroids (doughnuts), and the like, are generated by the rotation of lines or curves about an axis. *Polyhedra*, on the other hand, are formed by joining planar surfaces along edges that are defined by polygons. Since the time of the Greek philosopher Plato in the fourth century B.C., mathematicians have been fascinated with the properties of special polyhedra formed from *congruent regular polygons* with three, four, or five sides. Because only five such polyhedra are possible (and none can be formed from regular polygons with six or more sides), Plato believed that each one was associated with an element of the universe: earth, air, fire, water, and the universe itself. Below is a table of the properties of the *Platonic solids*.

Name	Face Shape	Faces	Edges	Vertices
Tetrahedron	triangle	4	6	4
Cube	square	6	12	8
Octahedron	triangle	8	12	6
Dodecahedron	pentagon	12	30	20
Icosahedron	triangle	20	30	12

Lessons 10.6–10.7

SURFACE AREA AND VOLUME OF SOLIDS The amount of material required to make a container is governed by the *surface area* of the container. The capacity of a container is given by its *volume*. An interesting student project is the investigation of shapes that contain the largest volume for a given amount of surface area.

CHAPTER 10

Tips for New Teachers
Use with Chapter 10.

Lesson 10.1

TEACHING TIP If you have not yet had students create a formulas page in their notebooks, now would be a good time to start. Each lesson of this chapter will introduce one or two new formulas to students.

The other formulas that students have studied this year include formulas for the area and the perimeter of rectangles and squares, the distance-rate-time formula, and the interest formula. As students record each formula, be sure they include why it is used and what the variables represent. It is also helpful for students to include a worked-out example of the formula somewhere near the formulas page.

COMMON ERROR For Example 2 on page 477, some students may not understand which of the two related division expressions is helpful: $b = 45 \div 9$, or $9 = 45 \div b$. Help students recognize that $b = 45 \div 9$ is the more helpful choice. Because b is equal to a numeric expression, students can find the value of b by evaluating the expression $45 \div 9$.

Lesson 10.2

INCLUSION For the benefit of your kinesthetic learners, help students see the relationship between the area of a parallelogram and the area of a triangle. Have students trace two congruent triangles similar to the one shown in the Notebook box on page 480. Have students cut out one of the triangles. By rotating the cutout triangle and placing it together with the other triangle, students can see that the two triangles form a parallelogram. Call students' attention to the fact that the height of the triangle equals the height of the parallelogram.

TEACHING TIP Standardized tests often contain test items that relate to composite figures. To deal with these items successfully, students need to understand the following facts about finding the area and the perimeter of composite figures.

To find the area of each composite figure, students need to add the areas of the parts.

- Area: The total area is the sum of the nonoverlapping parts.

To find the perimeters, students cannot total the perimeter of the parts, because this would include some interior segments. Instead, they need to add the lengths of the segments that form the outline of the figure.

- Perimeter: The perimeter of the figure does not include any interior line segments.

Lesson 10.3

INCLUSION *Circumference* will be a new word to some students. Relate the prefix *circum-* to the prefixes in words such as *circumnavigate* and *circumvent*. In all three cases, the prefix means *to go around*. To circumnavigate is to go around the world, especially by ship. To circumvent is to go around an obstacle, such as to *circumvent red tape*. *Circumference* means the distance going around a circle.

COMMON ERROR Often students select the wrong formula for circumference. They will use $C = \pi d$, when they should be using $C = 2\pi r$. Explain to students that the distance around every circle is just about three times the circle's diameter. Demonstrate this with many examples.

Emphasize that this relationship, the ratio of the circumference to the diameter, is described by about 3, or π (3.14). If students are given the radius of a circle, the radius must be doubled to get the diameter, before multiplying by π.

Lesson 10.4

INCLUSION To help students visualize the relationship between the radius of a circle and its area, have them draw a circle of radius 5 centimeters with the center at (0, 0) on centimeter graph paper. This circle should pass through the points (5, 0), (4, 3), (3, 4), and (0, 5) in the first quadrant. It should also pass through the symmetric points in the other three quadrants. After drawing the circle as accurately as possible, have students estimate the area by counting the number of square centimeters within the circle. They should get an estimate of about 76 cm², which is slightly greater than $3r^2$.

Tips for New Teachers

Use with Chapter 10.

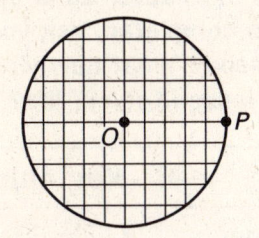

By drawing a square (that is $r \cdot r$), where $\overline{OP}$ is one side, students should see that a quarter of the circle has an area less than r^2, so the whole circle will have an area that is less than $4 \cdot r^2$. Therefore, the area of the circle is between $3r^2$ and $4r^2$. More precise measurements would give a value of πr^2, or about $3.14 \cdot r^2$.

Lesson 10.5

TEACHING TIP When discussing the classification of solids on page 500, have students note that a shaded region of a figure indicates that it is a base.

TEACHING TIP For Example 2, give students the pyramids in the table below. Have students determine the number of faces, edges, and vertices of each pyramid. The last figure in the table has hidden edges.

Figure	Faces	Vertices	Edges
	4	4	6
	6	6	10
	7	7	12
This pyramid's base has n sides.	$n + 1$	$n + 1$	$2n$

When completing the last row of the table, have students explain their reasoning. For example, when deciding on the number of faces, students should see that the pyramid will have n triangular faces and one base, for a total of $n + 1$ faces.

TEACHING TIP For Example 3, some students may find it easier to initially draw all edges as dashed lines. After all the lines are drawn, they can then select the lines that need to be solid and trace over them.

Lesson 10.6

INCLUSION For the activity on page 506, use the photocopier to enlarge the net to 400%. (Use the 200% enlargement twice.) Give each student one of the enlarged nets to cut out and form into a box. This will help the visual and kinesthetic learners in the classroom see exactly how the prism and its net are related.

COMMON ERROR For Exercises 16 and 17, some students will separate the composite solids into two prisms and add their surface areas, just as they found the areas of composite figures earlier in the chapter. Remind students that these prisms have part of one face in the interior of the composite solid. This face does not count as part of the surface area. Students also need to recognize that if they find these surface areas by adding the areas of the two prisms and by subtracting the area in the interior of the composite, they will need to subtract this area twice because it is part of both prisms.

Lesson 10.7

TEACHING TIP Use centimeter cubes to build rectangular solids. Have students determine the number of cubes in one layer and then in the total solid. This will help visual learners understand the relationship of the formula to the solid.

TEACHING TIP When discussing the volume of a rectangular prism with students, ask them to write a formula for a special type of prism—the cube. Students should recognize that the formula $V = s \cdot s \cdot s$ can be simplified to $V = s^3$.

TEACHING TIP Many times in this chapter, students have solved for a variable, using a formula. Earlier in the chapter, many of these problems could be solved using mental math. Now these problems are too difficult for most students to solve mentally. Watch carefully to see that all students can write out the steps.

CHAPTER 10

Name _____ Date _____

Parents as Partners

Use with Chapter 10.

Chapter Overview One way you can help your student succeed in Chapter 10 is by discussing the lesson goals in the chart below. When a lesson is completed, ask your student the following questions. "What were the goals of the lesson? What new words and formulas did you learn? How can you apply the ideas of the lesson to your life?"

Lesson Title	Lesson Goals	Key Applications
10.1: Area of a Parallelogram	Find the area of a parallelogram. Find an unknown dimension of a parallelogram.	• Lake Erie • Tennessee • Tangrams • Quilts
10.2: Area of a Triangle	Find the area of a triangle. Find the area of combined figures. Find the height or base of a triangle.	• Tall Ships • Pennants • Hang Gliders • Puerto Rican Flag
10.3: Circumference of a Circle	Find the circumference of a circle.	• Gym Wheel • Geology • Horse Training
10.4: Area of a Circle	Find the area of a circle. Compare areas of circles. Make a circle graph.	• Button Designs • Basketball • Pizza • Ski Trails • Lighthouse Beam
10.5: Solid Figures	Classify solids. Count faces, edges, and vertices. Draw a solid.	• Candles • Skateboard Jump
10.6: Surface Area of a Prism	Find the surface area of a prism.	• Jewelry Box • Cake Frosting • Piñata
10.7: Volume of a Prism	Find the volume of a rectangular prism. Use the volume formula to find an unknown dimension.	• Block Puzzles • Aquariums • Planters • Landing Pit

Know How to Take Notes

Learning to Use Formulas is the strategy featured in Chapter 10 (see page 474). Writing out each formula with a description and example helps your student to understand the formula. Having the information in your student's own words and handwriting provides cues for remembering the formula. Putting all the formulas in one location makes it easy to compare the ways and reasons that formulas are alike or different. Your student can then develop a regular routine for reviewing the formulas.

CHAPTER 10 Continued

Name _____ Date _____

Parents as Partners
Use with Chapter 10.

Key Ideas Your student can demonstrate understanding of key concepts by working through the following exercises with you.

Lesson	Exercise
10.1	The height of a parallelogram is 12 centimeters and the base is 5 centimeters. A second parallelogram has a height that is half as long and a base that is twice as long as the first parallelogram. Which parallelogram has a greater area?
10.2	A triangle has a height of 12 centimeters and a base of 5 centimeters. What happens to the area of the triangle if you triple the height of the triangle? the base?
10.3	Find the circumference of the circle with the given diameter or radius. Tell what value you used for π. Explain your choice. (a) $r = 8$ m (b) $d = 56$ in. (c) $d = 45$ ft (d) $r = 6.3$ mm
10.4	Find the area of each circle from the Lesson 10.3 Exercise to the nearest square unit.
10.5	Classify each solid. Then count the number of faces, edges, and vertices. (a) (b)
10.6	A tissue box is 11 centimeters wide, 11 centimeters long, and 14 centimeters high. Find the surface area of the box. *Bonus:* The circular opening in the top of the box has a diameter of 6 centimeters. Find the actual surface area of the box.
10.7	Find the volume of the tissue box from the Lesson 10.6 Exercise.

Home Involvement Activity

Directions: Find the volume of a room in your home. Next, find the volume of at least 3 items in the room. Then, find how much "free space" you have left over.

Answers

10.1: neither **10.2:** 30 cm^2; 90 cm^2 (it triples); 90 cm^2 (it triples) **10.3:** (a) 50.24 m (b) 176 in. (c) 141.3 ft (d) 39.6 mm (Used $\pi = \frac{22}{7}$ for (b) and (d) because the numbers were divisible by 7. **10.4:** (a) 201 m^2 (b) 2464 in^2 (c) 1590 ft^2 (d) 125 mm^2 **10.5:** (a) triangular prism: 5, 9, 6 (b) rectangular prism: 6, 12, 8 **10.6:** 858 cm^2; *Bonus:* 829.74 cm^2 **10.7:** 1694 cm^3

Middle School Math, Course 1 97
Professional Development Book

Chapter 10

Bulletin Board Idea

Use with Chapter 10.

Objective

To visually reinforce the concept of the surface area of a solid figure and the relationship between solid figures and their nets.

Materials

- 4 sentence strips
- 8 index cards
- 4 pieces of construction paper
- pushpins

Constructing the Bulletin Board

1. On the first sentence strip, write the title of the bulletin board, "Solid Figures and Their Surface Areas." Enlarge each net, so that the side of each square is 4 inches. Tape the enlargments onto the four pieces of construction paper. Arrange these nets on the bulletin board with the title above them.

2. On four of the index cards, sketch the figure that each net will form. On the other index cards, write the names of the four solids: cube, rectangular prism, triangular prism, and square pyramid. Place these around the bulletin board with pushpins.

3. On three sentence strips, write the following sentences.
   - Match the pattern to the solid you would get by folding each pattern.
   - Match the pattern to the name of the figure it would form.
   - What is the surface area of each solid? How do you know?

Using the Bulletin Board

After students complete Lesson 10.5, discuss the bulletin board and its questions with the class. The discussion and the solution to the problems may include the following.

- Tell students that all the triangles and all the squares in the nets are congruent. Have them measure the sides of one square and calculate its area. Then have them measure the base and height of one triangle and calculate its area.

- If you have used the dimensions suggested above, the area of each square is 16 square inches and the area of each triangle is 8 square inches. Students can then find the area of each figure using these areas.

Follow-up

- Have students challenge each other by creating other nets and sketching their solids. They should also have their classmates determine the surface areas of the solid.

Middle School Math, Course 1
Professional Development Book

CHAPTER 11
Math Behind the Math
Use with Chapter 11.

Lesson 11.1

COMPARING INTEGERS The set of numbers known as *integers* includes zero and all counting numbers (1, 2, 3, 4, . . .) and their opposites. Zero is set apart from all other numbers because it is neither positive nor negative; it is simply a starting point or a frame of reference for all other integers. The counting numbers (1, 2, 3, 4, . . .) and the whole numbers (0, 1, 2, 3, 4 . . .) are subsets of the set of integers (. . . −4, −3, −2, −1, 0, 1, 2, 3, 4, . . .).

The introduction of the "−" sign to a counting number, such as 5, 6, or 7, suggests that a number can have a direction associated with it. Using a visual, such as a number line, is an invaluable tool for understanding the value of an integer or for comparing the value of two integers. Associating a direction with a number is a very important concept in higher mathematics.

For any two places on a number line, the integer on the right is greater than the integer on the left. The integer on the left is less than the integer on the right. Using a number line helps students visualize the order of negative numbers. Without a number line, it can be difficult to see, for example, that −2 is greater than −30.

Lessons 11.2–11.3

ADDING INTEGERS When adding integers that have the same sign, add the numbers' *absolute values* and retain the same sign.

$$-14 + -5 = -(14 + 5) = -19$$

When adding integers that have different signs, subtract the numbers' absolute values and retain the sign of the number with the greater absolute value.

$$-14 + 5 = -(14 - 5) = -9$$

To model addition of integers on a number line, use arrows pointing to the right for positive integers and arrows pointing to the left for negative integers. A defining property of integers, $a + (-a) = 0$, is represented by one arrow extending from 0 to a and a second arrow extending from a to 0. Thus, the sum of an integer and its opposite "cancel" each other out.

SUBTRACTING INTEGERS Subtracting an integer is the same as *adding its opposite*. First, rewrite the subtraction expression as an addition expression then use the rules for adding integers.

For example,

$$-5 - (-3) = -5 + 3$$
$$= -2$$

To model integer subtraction on a number line, use the fact that subtraction is the direct opposite of addition. To subtract −3 from a number, such as in the example above, remember that −3 is modeled by an arrow pointing to the left. Then *subtracting* −3 is modeled by an arrow pointing to the right. To show −5 − (−3), use one arrow extending from 0 to −5 and a second arrow extending from −5 three units to the right. It ends at −2, which represents the difference.

Lessons 11.4–11.5

MULTIPLYING AND DIVIDING INTEGERS Keeping track of the sign when multiplying or dividing mixed positive and negative values can be confusing. It can be very helpful to memorize the rules for multiplying and dividing integers.

Rules for Multiplying Integers				
+	×	+	=	+
−	×	−	=	+
+	×	−	=	−
−	×	+	=	−

Rules for Dividing Integers				
+	÷	+	=	+
−	÷	−	=	+
+	÷	−	=	−
−	÷	+	=	−

A good principle to remember is that multiplication or division by a *positive* factor or divisor does *not* cause a change from the sign of the original number, but multiplication or division by a *negative* factor or divisor *does* cause a change from the sign of the original number.

Middle School Math, Course 1
Professional Development Book

Math Behind the Math

Use with Chapter 11.

Lesson 11.6

COORDINATE PLANE With the introduction of the coordinate plane, mathematics is extended into a second dimension. To be complete, the two-dimensional coordinate plane has two perpendicular number lines that intersect at (0,0), called the origin, and labeled O. Coordinates extend to infinity in both the positive and the negative directions.

A major use of coordinate systems is to locate points given by coordinates. On a number line, the coordinate is a single value. In a two-dimensional coordinate system, points are identified by ordered pairs. Ordered pairs give the position of the point relative to the horizontal and the vertical axes. This is the basis for all two-dimensional graphing.

Students have already learned to recognize translations, where an object is moved over a certain distance in one dimension. On a coordinate plane, plane figures can be defined by the coordinates of their vertices. This makes it possible to mathematically "slide" a plane figure from one location to another without its size or orientation being altered. Applying the same change to each of the coordinates that defines the figure slides the figure across the plane. Again, negative coordinates allow for such translations in any direction to any location on the plane.

Lesson 11.7

REFLECTIONS AND ROTATIONS Mathematically, *reflections* behave very much like images in a mirror. In mathematics, the reflection of a two-dimensional object is its image flipped over a *line of reflection*. Like a transformation, a reflection does not alter the size or shape of an object. Its parts are simply reversed about the line symmetry.

The diagram below shows how a reflection and a mirror image are equivalent ideas.

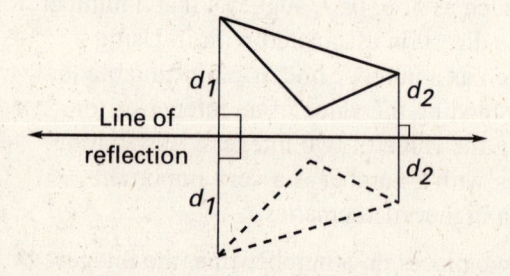

The two triangles are reflections, or mirror images, of each other. Every corresponding pair of points is an equal distance, d, from the line of reflection.

A *rotation* occurs when a figure is turned about a stationary point, either on or off the figure. Note how the result of a rotation is very different from a reflection. Corresponding points on rotated objects are equal distances from a single fixed point, not from the line.

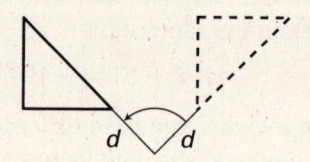

Chapter 11: Tips for New Teachers

Use with Chapter 11.

Lesson 11.1

TEACHING TIP *Integers*, *absolute value*, and *opposites* are new terms for many students. Make a point of defining and then reviewing these terms often. Be sure that students understand that the opposite of a *negative number* is a *positive number*. Explain that a negative sign represents the opposite of a number. The expression $-(-8)$ means "the opposite of negative 8." The opposite of negative 8 is positive 8, so $-(-8) = 8$.

COMMON ERROR For Example 3 on page 534, some students may tell you that -8 should be greater than -5, because 8 is greater than 5. To show students that indeed $-5 > -8$ is the more consistent interpretation, have them consider the financial well-being of someone who has borrowed some money. Negative numbers represent money borrowed. Students know generally that a better financial condition is represented by $-\$5$ than by $-\$8$. If loan amounts closer to zero are better to have than loan amounts farther from 0, then negative numbers closer to zero are greater than negative numbers farther from 0. So, $-\$5 > -\$8$.

Lesson 11.2

INCLUSION For Example 1 on page 538, have your kinesthetic learners draw the number line for the sums in their notebooks. Be sure students understand that positive numbers are represented by arrows pointing in the positive direction and that negative numbers are represented by arrows pointing in the negative direction. Students also need to understand that the second arrow begins where the first arrow stops. Additionally, the third arrow begins where the second arrow stops.

TEACHING TIP When you review the Notebook guide for adding integers on page 539, some students may become confused by the concept of "subtracting" in order "to add."

To help them see why "subtracting" gives the sum of two numbers, break apart the addend with the greater absolute value. For example, with a problem such as $7 + (-10)$, break apart the -10, as shown.

$$7 + (-10) = 7 + [(-7) + (-3)]$$
$$= [7 + (-7)] + (-3)$$
$$= 0 + (-3) = -3$$

The positive 7 combines with the negative 7 to make 0. So, -3 is all that remains.

Lesson 11.3

TEACHING TIP Have students compare the number line models for subtraction and addition. Check that students understand in which direction to move for each number. For example, compare the sum $2 + (-3)$ to the difference $2 - (-3)$, as shown below.

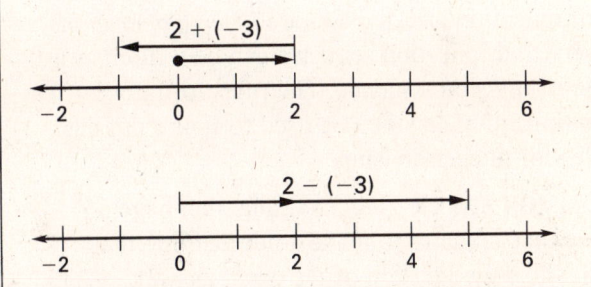

TEACHING TIP When students are first working with subtracting integers without number lines, encourage them to rewrite every subtraction problem using the following method.

$$5 - 6 \qquad 5 + \underline{\ ?\ } \qquad 5 + \underline{(-6)}$$

As students rewrite the subtraction problems as addition problems, ask them to speak out the rewriting process.

"The expression *5 minus 6* is the same as *5 plus the opposite of positive 6*. So, I write *5 plus negative 6*."

After students have rewritten the subtraction problems as addition problems, ask them to use the rules for adding integers.

Lesson 11.4

TEACHING TIP You may want to point out to students which keys on their calculators are used to input negative numbers. On some calculators, they may need to input (−) 8, and on others, it will be 8 +/−.

CHAPTER 11 Continued

Tips for New Teachers
Use with Chapter 11.

TEACHING TIP Because multiplication by a positive number is repeated addition, you can illustrate the product of a negative and a positive number on a number line. For example, to show $3 \cdot (-2)$, use three arrows as shown below.

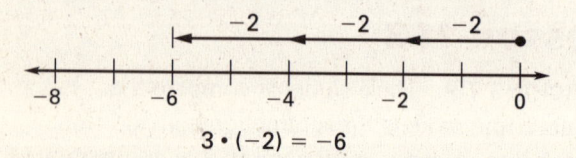

$$3 \cdot (-2) = -6$$

Lesson 11.5

TEACHING TIP Remind students that multiplication and division are *inverse operations*. Every multiplication sentence can be written as a related division sentence. The rules for integer multiplication can then be used to figure out the rules for integer division.

COMMON ERROR For Example 3 on page 555, challenge students to make a number line that will show the location of the exact answer, -7.3. Some students may place it to the right of -7, because they are accustomed to finding a mixed number to the right of its whole number part. However, with negative mixed numbers, the mixed number will be to the left of the whole number part. For example, -7.3 is to the left of -7, because it is located between -7 and -8.

Lesson 11.6

TEACHING TIP Remind students that a *plane* is a surface that extends forever in all directions. To identify any point on the plane, two intersecting number lines, called the *axes*, are placed on the plane to establish a grid. This grid is called a *coordinate plane*.

Ordered pairs are used to name the points in the plane. Remind students that the first number of an ordered pair locates a point along the *x*-axis. It tells how far right ($+$) or left ($-$) of the origin the point is. The second number further defines the location of that point on the *y*-axis. It tells how far up ($+$) or down ($-$) from the origin the point is.

TEACHING TIP Students may be familiar with *translations*, but not with the term itself. Elementary level textbooks commonly use the term *slides*. At earlier grade levels, however, students generally will not have seen translations along a coordinate plane. For Example 3, be sure students understand that every point of the figure has moved 4 units right and 5 units down, even though they have only found the new coordinates of four points. For example, the point (2.5, 6.5) on $\overline{DC}$ has moved to (6.5, 1.5) on $\overline{SR}$.

INCLUSION To motivate your visual students, ask students to bring to class examples of translations that they find in their home or in other classes. Some places they can look for these examples are in photos of architectural details on buildings, such as the moldings, and in home fabrics, such as table linens, quilts, and handwoven rugs. A common use of translations is in the creation of tessellations, in which one or more figures are translated repeatedly to cover a plane.

Lesson 11.7

TEACHING TIP An important connection that you should help students make is the connection between the *symmetric* figures in Lesson 9.8 and the *reflections* in this lesson. To help students see this connection, draw a symmetric figure such as the one below. Make the top half red and the bottom half blue. Draw *a line of symmetry* to divide the figure. This should help students see that although this is a single figure, one half is the mirror image of the other half.

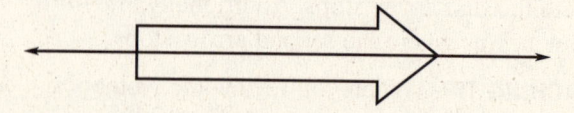

INCLUSION To help students visualize rotations of 180°, bring to class the blank grid from the crossword puzzle in your daily or Sunday newspaper. Show students how each black figure has a matching figure that is rotated 180° about the center of the puzzle. Have students make a similar crossword puzzle design on grid paper.

102 Middle School Math, Course 1
Professional Development Book

Chapter 11

Name _____ Date _____

Parents as Partners
Use with Chapter 11.

Chapter Overview One way you can help your student succeed in Chapter 11 is by discussing the lesson goals in the chart below. When a lesson is completed, ask your student the following questions. "What were the goals of the lesson? What new words and formulas did you learn? How can you apply the ideas of the lesson to your life?"

Lesson	Lesson Goals	Key Applications
11.1: Comparing Integers	Compare and order integers. Identify opposites.	• Space Shuttles • Scuba Divers • In-Line Skating • Temperatures
11.2: Adding Integers	Add integers. Model integer addition.	• Football • Stock Value • Game Shows
11.3: Subtracting Integers	Subtract integers. Model integer subtraction.	• Mauna Loa • Cooking • Sunken Ships
11.4: Multiplying Integers	Multiply integers. Evaluate expressions.	• Bay of Fundy • Diving • Bears
11.5: Dividing Integers	Divide integers. Find the mean of integers.	• Antarctica • Golf • Global Temperatures
11.6: Translations in a Coordinate Plane	Graph points with negative coordinates. Translate a figure.	• Animation • Map • Tornados
11.7: Reflections and Rotations	Recognize reflections and rotations.	• Photography • Weaving

Know How to Take Notes

Using Multiple Representations is the strategy featured in Chapter 11 (see page 532). Encourage your student to record numbers in different forms in order to illustrate new concepts. Recording numbers this way helps foster understanding of the numbers and how they can be used. The more your student works with numbers, the greater his/her comprehension will be.

Middle School Math, Course 1   103
Professional Development Book

Chapter 11 Continued

Name _____ **Date** _____

Parents as Partners
Use with Chapter 11.

Key Ideas Your student can demonstrate understanding of key concepts by working through the following exercises with you.

Lesson	Exercise
11.1	In golf, the lowest score wins the match. Four students played a round of miniature golf and kept track of their scores against par. At the end of the round, Juan was 1 under par, Amelia was 3 over par, Andrea was 2 under par, and Carlos was 2 over par. Write the scores as integers in order from least to greatest. Who won?
11.2	Your scores (against par) for nine holes of golf were 0, −2, −1, 0, 2, 2, 1, 0, and −1. What was your total score?
11.3	Nick was taking pictures of Tanya climbing down a cliff. He took a picture of her 16 feet above him. She climbed down 23 feet and he took another. He took a third picture after she had climbed down another 14 feet. What was Tanya's height relative to Nick's in the second and third pictures?
11.4	Evaluate the expression when $x = -4$ and $y = -1$. (a) $3x$ (b) $7y$ (c) xy
11.5	Find the quotient. (a) $15 \div (-3)$ (b) $-72 \div (-18)$ (c) $-144 \div 16$
11.6	Graph the points $A(2, 8)$, $B(5, 6)$, $C(5, 1)$, and $D(2, 3)$ on a coordinate plane and connect them to form quadrilateral $ABCD$. Translate the quadrilateral 3 units to the left and 4 units down to form quadrilateral $EFGH$. Give the coordinates of the vertices of the image.
11.7	(a) Graph quadrilateral $ABCD$ from the previous question on a coordinate plane. Reflect the figure over the x-axis to form quadrilateral $IJKL$. Give the coordinates of the vertices of the image. (b) Graph quadrilateral $ABCD$ on a new coordinate plane. Rotate the figure clockwise 90° about the origin to form quadrilateral $QRST$. Give the coordinates of the vertices of the image.

Home Involvement Activity

Directions: Look around your home or neighborhood to find real-life examples of congruent figures that could be described as transformations of each other. Describe at least one of each type of transformation you have studied.

Answers

11.1: −2, −1, 2, 3; Andrea 11.2: 1 11.3: 7 feet below Nick; 21 feet below Nick 11.4: (a) −12 (b) −7 (c) 4 11.5: (a) −5 (b) 4 (c) −9 11.6: $E(-1, 4)$, $F(2, 2)$, $G(2, -3)$, $H(-1, -1)$ 11.7: (a) $I(2, -8)$, $J(5, -6)$, $K(5, -1)$, $L(2, -3)$ (b) $Q(8, -2)$, $R(6, -5)$, $S(1, -5)$, $T(3, -2)$

104 Middle School Math, Course 1
Professional Development Book

Bulletin Board Idea

Use with Chapter 11.

Objective

To visually reinforce the concepts of reflection, rotation, and symmetry.

Materials

- 2 sheets of construction paper
- 4 sentence strips

Constructing the Bulletin Board

1. Use the diagram of the tangram to create two sets of tangram pieces from construction paper. Arrange one set of tangram pieces in a square as shown. Place it on the left side of the bulletin board. Then use the other set to create an interesting figure set in the center of the bulletin board.

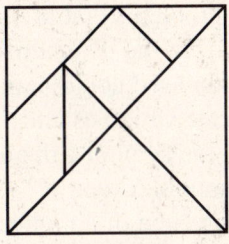

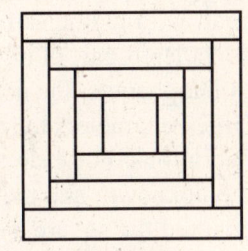

    Tangram

    Log Cabin Quilt Pattern

2. Copy the quilt pattern onto construction paper and color it to create a pleasing quilt square. Mount the pattern on the board to the right of the tangram pieces.

3. On one sentence strip, write the title, "Symmetry Patterns." On the other three sentence strips, write the following questions:

    - What other figures can you create using the tangram pieces?
    - What basic shapes are used to create this quilt square?
    - What other examples of symmetry can you find in the world around you?

Using the Bulletin Board

After students complete Lesson 11.7, discuss the bulletin board and its questions with the class. Explain that reflection, rotation, and symmetry can be found everywhere in the world around us. The discussion may include the following points.

- Tangrams use basic shapes that have line symmetry or point symmetry to create interesting patterns and designs. The number of patterns that can be created by the 10 pieces is almost endless. Have students create other shapes and patterns using the tangram pieces.

- Most quilt block patterns are made of basic shapes like squares, rectangles, triangles, and parallelograms. By using repeating shapes with reflection and rotation, quilt designers can create beautiful designs that often, but not always, exhibit symmetry.

Follow-up

- Have students pick a set of three or four basic shapes and use them to create their own unique quilt square. They should draw it on a piece of paper and color it in. Display the quilt squares around the room.

- Have students look through magazines or sources to find examples of symmetry, rotation, and reflection. Students should bring in pictures to be added to the bulletin board.

CHAPTER 12
Math Behind the Math

Use with Chapter 12.

Lessons 12.1–12.4

HISTORICAL ALGEBRAIC SYMBOLS AND NOTATION The language of mathematics has developed by bits and pieces over the centuries. In early mathematics, the collection of symbols that we now call *notation* was very different from what we recognize in algebraic expressions today. Diophantus of Alexandria (A.D. 250), dealt with mathematical problems that are now considered part of algebra. In the texts attributed to Diophantus, the notation used combinations of Greek characters to indicate variables and operations. For example, the symbol ζ denoted the unknown, and the symbols Δ^γ and K^γ denoted the square and the cube of a number. The mathematics communicated by symbols like these would be unrecognizable to most people today. Centuries later, the system of symbols and expression that we now use began to emerge.

The most important mathematician related to algebra is al-Khowarizmi. His treatises on Hindu arithmetic and on algebra made him famous. It is believed that he gave algebra its name and that the word *algorithm* may have been derived from his own name. Much of the mathematical knowledge of medieval Europe was derived from Latin translations of his works. Unlike the Greek mathematicians, al-Khowarizmi did not use symbols for particular arithmetic operations.

MODERN EXPRESSIONS AND EQUATIONS Our modern mathematical symbols (like + and −) began to appear as early as the fourteenth century A.D. With the invention of printed books in the fifteenth century, however, an explosion in communication followed. Clear and consistent ways to express mathematical language became more important.

By the seventeenth century, most of today's common symbols (+, −, ÷, =, and so on) were in regular use. René Descartes (1596–1650) was the first mathematician to make consistent use of the symbols *x*, *y*, and *z* to represent unknowns. His composition, *La géométrie*, linked algebra and geometry and is perhaps the earliest text in which the modern student of mathematics would recognize and follow the mathematical notations.

WRITING EXPRESSIONS A good part of the challenge that students face with algebra is translating the circumstances of a problem into *expressions* and *equations*. In these lessons, attention is restricted mainly to *linear* expressions and equations. This means that the unknown, or *variable*, in the expression has an exponent of 1 — there are no squares, cubes, or higher exponents of the variable in the expression. The table below shows some examples of problems that involve simple linear expressions.

Operation	Example	Expression
addition	3 gallons of water added to an unknown amount	$x + 3$
subtraction	the withdrawal of an unknown amount from a $50 bank account	$50 - w$
multiplication	the distance traveled at a speed of 60 mi/h for an unknown time	$60t$
division	a pizza of unknown area cut into four pieces	$\dfrac{x}{4}$

SOLUTIONS Algebra is about finding a *solution* to a problem. Students should have a firm grasp of the goal when seeking the solution for an unknown in an equation. That goal is *to find the value of the unknown that makes the equation true*.

CHAPTER 12 Continued
Math Behind the Math

Use with Chapter 12.

Problem	Equation	Solution
To how much water does adding 3 more gallons of water result in a total of 8 gallons?	$x + 3 = 8$	$x = 5$
The withdrawal of how much money from a $50 bank account leaves $30?	$50 - w = 30$	$w = 20$
How many hours of time are needed to travel 180 miles at a constant speed of 60 mi/h?	$60t = 180$	$t = \dfrac{180}{60}$ $t = 3$
What is the total area in square centimeters of a pizza cut into four pieces of 900 square centimeters each?	$\dfrac{A}{4} = 900$	$A = 4 \times 900$ $A = 3600$

Lessons 12.5–12.6

FUNCTIONS Mathematics offers powerful tools for modeling and for keeping track of changing quantities by using *functions*. At this grade level, attention is limited to first order, or *linear* functions of one variable. This means that every variable in the function has an exponent of 1. It is possible to have functions of two or more variables, or even functions that return multivariable values. However, those will be discussed in later courses.

For a simple example of a linear function of one variable, consider a car that is traveling at a constant speed of 60 mi/h. The distance traveled in miles from a starting point where time is equal to 0 *as a function of* elapsed time in hours is written:

$f(t) = 60t$

Note that it is very important to carefully define the units and the starting point to make sure functions are valid. If the starting point was 18 miles up the road when time was 0, then the function would look slightly different.

$f(t) = 60t + 18$

GRAPHING FUNCTIONS The graph of a linear function is a straight line. The steepness, or *slope*, of the graph of a linear function is greater if the number multiplying the variable is greater. If the function has any powers of the variable greater than the first, the graph will be curved. Computers and graphing calculators offer powerful tools for quickly making graphs. Below is a sample plot of $f(t) = 60t$. Students may be able to predict what such a graph would look like for the function $f(t) = 60t + 18$. (It would look the same, except that the whole line would move up so that the starting point is at 18 miles.)

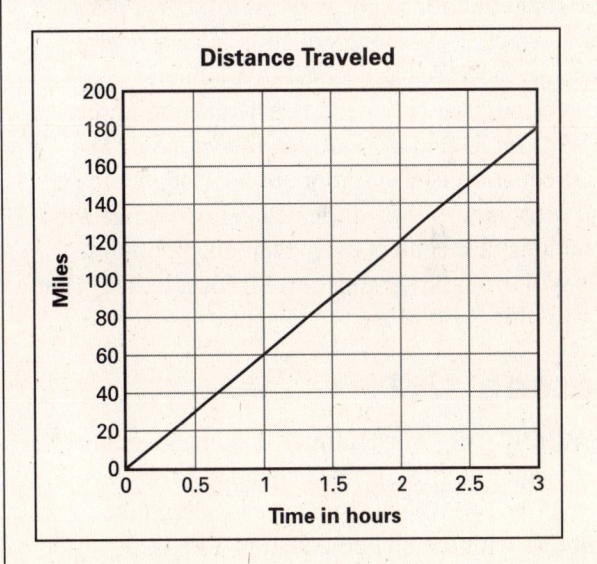

Distance Traveled

[Graph showing a straight line from (0, 0) to (3, 180), with x-axis labeled "Time in hours" from 0 to 3 and y-axis labeled "Miles" from 0 to 200.]

Chapter 12 Tips for New Teachers
Use with Chapter 12.

Lesson 12.1

TEACHING TIP Help students decide whether an equation or an expression is needed for a particular situation. Remind them that an expression models a phrase and an equation models a complete sentence. A situation that is represented by an equation (or inequality) always contains a verb, such as *is*, *equals*, or *is less than*. A situation that is represented by an expression does not contain these verbs.

TEACHING TIP When writing equations for problems such as Example 4 on page 584, many equivalent equations are possible. Have students write all the equations that model this situation, stressing that *all* three of the following are appropriate.

$$3 = \frac{27}{a} \qquad a = \frac{27}{3} \qquad 3a = 27$$

The first equation is not very useful, but it is still correct. The second equation is very useful. Because the variable is equal to a numeric expression, you only need to evaluate the numeric expression to find the value of the variable. The third equation is also important for students to see and recognize. When students begin working with equations that contain more than one operation, this will often be the most useful form to use. That is why this form is used in the student text.

Lesson 12.2

TEACHING TIP For Example 2, some students may want to write a related equation to solve $y + 25 = 140$. While students can solve this problem with the related equation $140 - 25 = y$, explain to them that this method will not work well solving more complex equations, such as $7x + 15 = 10x - 9$. Encourage hesitant students to learn this new method of writing equations.

COMMON ERROR For Example 2, some students will add 25 to both sides of the equation because they see the plus sign in the equation. Remind students that solving equations is a way of working backward to find out what the value of the variable is, and working backward always uses inverse operations. While many students can easily solve these simple problems mentally, you should encourage them to record each step. This will increase their level of success when the problems become more challenging.

Lesson 12.3

COMMON ERROR When some students solve equations such as $14 = n - 6$, they may add the constant term 14 to both sides of the equation, instead of the 6. When they try to do this, they will get "stuck" and not know what to do next. Emphasize to students that when solving an equation, they need to get the variable alone on one side of the equation. To get the variable, n, by itself they must add 6 to each side of the equation.

INCLUSION For kinesthic learners, have students work in pairs to play a game using subtraction equations. Give each student pair a number cube. Have one player roll the number cube twice. Have this player use the numbers rolled to write an equation in one of the two following forms.

$x - $ first roll $=$ second roll

first roll $= x - $ second roll

The second player then solves the equations. The first player checks the solutions. Then have students switch roles. Have students play as many rounds as time allows.

Lesson 12.4

TEACHING TIP To model a division equation, you can use a variable tile to represent a fractional part of a variable. For example, to model $\frac{x}{3} = 4$, use the following steps.

Then you know that the following is true.

So, $x = 12$.

108 Middle School Math, Course 1
Professional Development Book

Chapter 12 Continued: Tips for New Teachers
Use with Chapter 12.

TEACHING TIP For Example 3, you may want students to write a verbal model to obtain the equation. The verbal model would look like the following.

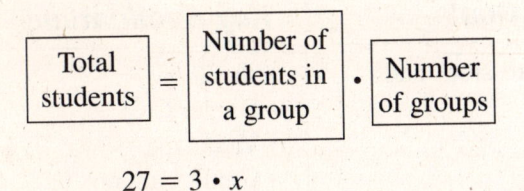

$$\boxed{\text{Total students}} = \boxed{\text{Number of students in a group}} \cdot \boxed{\text{Number of groups}}$$

$$27 = 3 \cdot x$$

After solving the equation, have students check the answer in the context of the equation. Then they can be sure the answer is reasonable.

Lesson 12.5

TEACHING TIP To help students see the connection between number patterns and functions, use the table shown in Example 1. The number pattern in the third column of the table shows 30, 60, 90, and 120. Students should be able to continue the pattern very quickly by skip counting 30, 60, 90, 120, 150, 180, 210, and so on.

Tell students that skip counting is a good way to find the number of pounds of bamboo that a panda eats in a few days. But if information about the number of pounds of bamboo is needed for a whole month or an entire year, skip counting is very inefficient. A *function* works better.

INCLUSION To help your visual learners, give students graph paper and have them create geometric patterns of their own, similar to the following pattern.

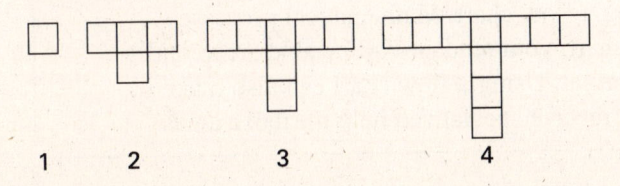

1   2   3   4

Next, have students write a number pattern for the geometric pattern they create. Finally have students write a rule for the number pattern. If writing the number pattern is difficult, suggest that they write a "close to" pattern of multiples. For the example above, they can make a table like the one below.

Pattern Number (x)	Number of Boxes (y)	"Close to" Pattern of Multiples
1	1	3
2	4	6
3	7	9
4	10	12

The pattern of "close to" multiples is $y = 3x$. From this pattern, the pattern for the number of boxes is $y = 3x - 2$.

Lesson 12.6

COMMON ERROR When students are learning how to graph a function, Step 2, in Example 1, may be a stumbling block because some students do not comprehend why the rows of the table are becoming ordered pairs. For these students, note that no mathematical property exists to justify this step. Rather, they are simply writing the rows of the table in the form (input, output) just to see what information the new form will give.

TEACHING TIP As students examine the many ways to represent a function on page 613, they should understand that the list of ordered pairs and the input-output table show only a few representative points of the function. The other forms represent an infinite number of solutions to the problem.

CHAPTER 12

Name _____ Date _____

Parents as Partners
Use with Chapter 12.

Chapter Overview One way you can help your student succeed in Chapter 12 is by discussing the lesson goals in the chart below. When a lesson is completed, ask your student the following questions. "What were the goals of the lesson? What new words and formulas did you learn? How can you apply the ideas of the lesson to your life?"

Lesson Title	Lesson Goals	Key Applications
12.1: Writing Expressions and Equations	Write variable expressions and equations.	• Art Show • Dinner Cost • Videotape • Grand Canyon
12.2: Solving Addition Equations	Solve one-step addition equations. Use an addition equation.	• Shopping • Video Game • Parking Meter • Marathon Training
12.3: Solving Subtraction Equations	Solve one-step subtraction equations. Use a subtraction equation.	• Shell Collection • Elevator • Berries • Paper Route
12.4: Solving Multiplication and Division Equations	Solve one-step multiplication and division equations. Use an equation.	• Cheerleading • Pens • Hurricanes
12.5: Functions	Evaluate functions and write function rules.	• Giant Pandas • School Dance • A Road Trip
12.6: Graphing Functions	Graph linear functions in a coordinate plane. Identify linear functions.	• Walking • Ski Lift • Sign Painting

How to Take Notes

Making a Flow Chart is the strategy featured in Chapter 12 (see page 582). Encourage your student to show various mathematical processes using a flow chart. Mathematical processes require a number of steps to solve. By using a flow chart, your student will be able "map out" each step that is needed in a logical and organized format. Using a flow chart can also make it easier for your student to identify problem areas and receive specialized help for those areas.

CHAPTER 12 Continued

Parents as Partners
Use with Chapter 12.

Key Ideas Your student can demonstrate understanding of key concepts by working through the following exercises with you.

Lesson	Exercise
12.1	You were recently dog sitting for your neighbors. You charged them $5 each day for feeding and walking the dog. The amount they owed you when they returned was $75. Write an equation you could use to find the number of days d you watched the dog.
12.2	Your neighbors owed you $75 for dog sitting, but they gave you $89. Write and solve an addition equation to find the amount t of your tip.
12.3	Your neighbors left you money to buy dog food while they were gone. The dog food cost $7.93 and you had $2.07 left over after buying dog food. Write and solve a subtraction equation for the amount of money m your neighbors left you.
12.4	Solve your equation from the Lesson 12.1 question.
12.5	Make an input-output table for the baby-sitting jobs listed below, using the hours worked h as the input and the amount paid p as the output. Then write a function rule that relates h and p. Job #1: paid: $12; worked: 2 hours Job #2: paid: $18; worked: 3 hours Job #3: paid: $24; worked: 4 hours Job #4: paid: $36; worked: 6 hours
12.6	Graph your function from the Lesson 12.5 question. Determine if the function is linear or not.

Home Involvement Activity

Directions: Each time you watch television in the next week, record the number of minutes you spend watching and the number of commercials that are on. Make your data into ordered pairs, and graph the points. Do the points appear to be on a line? Can you predict how many commercials you will see based on how many minutes of television you watch?

Answers

12.1: $5d = 75$ 12.2: $75 + t = 89$; $14   12.3: $m - 7.93 = 2.07$; $10.00   12.4: 15 days

12.5:
Input h	2	3	4	6
Output p	12	18	24	36

$p = 6h$ 12.6: Yes, the function is linear.

Middle School Math, Course 1   111
Professional Development Book

CHAPTER 12

Bulletin Board Idea

Use with Chapter 12.

Objective

To use the information from the Unit 4 poster to write a conversion formula for degrees Celsius to degrees Fahrenheit, and to use the formula to solve problems

Materials

- 3 sentence strips
- colored yarn
- Unit 4 poster: Mt. Rainier

Constructing the Bulletin Board

1. Write out three sentence strips. The first is the title, "Why does $C = \frac{5}{9}(F - 32)$ convert degrees Fahrenheit to degrees Celsius?" The second should read, "Boiling Point of Water at Sea Level." The third should read, "Freezing Point of Water at Sea Level."

2. Place the title strip at the top of the bulletin board. Position the poster below the title. Place the second and third sentence strips to the right of the poster.

3. Add the yarn to create pointers. One piece of yarn should connect the second sentence strip to the boiling point of water on the thermometer diagrams. Another piece of yarn should connect the third sentence strip to the freezing point of water.

Using the Bulletin Board

After students complete Lesson 12.5, discuss the bulletin board and its question with the class. The discussion and the solution to the problem may include the following points.

- 0° Celsius and 32° Fahrenheit are measures of the same temperature (freezing), and 100° Celsius and 212° Fahrenheit are also measures of the same temperature (boiling).

- The range of temperatures from 0°C to 100°C is the same temperature range as from 32°F to 212°F. If you compare the range of Celsius readings to the range of Fahrenheit readings for the same temperatures, you get a ratio of 100 : 180, or 5 : 9. For every 1° Fahrenheit that the temperature rises or falls, it rises or falls $\frac{5}{9}$° Celsius.

- If you start with the lower end of the scale, you can see that any function that starts with an input of 32 and ends up with an output of 0 cannot involve just multiplying or dividing. Therefore, the conversion formula must start by subtracting 32 from the Fahrenheit reading (F). However, since the ratio of one degree Celsius to one degree Fahrenheit is $\frac{5}{9}$, subtracting 32 only gives a correct conversion if the Fahrenheit temperature is exactly 32°. To find the correct number of degrees above or below 0° Celsius, add $\frac{5}{9}$°C for every 1°F. To do that, you multiply $F - 32$ by $\frac{5}{9}$.

Follow-up

- Ask students to write an equation for converting degrees Celsius to degrees Fahrenheit. ($F = \frac{9}{5}C + 32$). Then have students use a scientific reference to find the boiling point of a few common gases, such as oxygen, hydrogen, and nitrogren, given in degrees Celsius. Have students convert the temperatures to degrees Fahrenheit.

Middle School Math, Course 1
Professional Development Book

Chapter 13: Math Behind the Math

Use with Chapter 13.

Lessons 13.1–13.3

RANDOM EVENTS AND PROBABILITY The study of probability helps us figure out the likelihood of something happening. The nature of random events within the context of everyday life is greatly misunderstood by most people, leading to many inappropriate beliefs and superstitions. For this reason, a thorough instruction in probability is essential to a good education in mathematics.

An event is *random* if it produces different possible *outcomes* that can vary from one repetition to another. Types of random events vary. One roll of a six-sided die is a random event, where each of the outcomes 1, 2, ... 6, has a probability of $\frac{1}{6}$. The time period during which an atom may or may not experience radioactive decay is another kind of random event, where the possible outcomes (the atom decays during the time period, or it does not) have *specific probabilities*. These are just two examples of the many possible random events.

So, the probability, or "chance," that a specific outcome will occur is often calculable and measurable. For example, tossing a *fair* coin, one that is *equally likely* to land showing heads or tails when tossed, will produce an outcome of heads with a probability of $\frac{1}{2}$, or 0.5. This means that in the long run, heads (or tails) will occur half of the time.

This explanation of randomness suggests a very important aspect of probability — the *actual* number of successes in repeated observations of an event converge to the number expected by the *theoretical* probability of success "in the long run," meaning a *very large number of trials*. This is known as the *law of large numbers*. Students should be able to provide an explanation, given the following question: If a fair coin-toss experiment was conducted, and heads came up seven times in a row, was the theory of probability violated? *No*. Randomness allows for variations, including unlikely, or *rare*, outcomes. In fact, it is possible to calculate probabilities for rare events, like "seven heads in a row."

An excellent way to start thinking about randomness and probability is to create a list of some of the events in daily life that have random properties. Such a list may include weather, sports, and games. The list should illustrate that randomness affects events both in both nature and in human activities. Students who go on to study physical science will learn that modern explanations of the behavior of matter itself, including quantum, nuclear, and thermal physics, depend on probabilistic and statistical models.

INDEPENDENCE Before deciding how to count possible outcomes, it is necessary to figure out whether one outcome influences another. For example, each coin flip in a series of flips is an *independent event* — the appearance of heads or tails in one flip is not influenced by what happens in any other flip.

On the other hand, in a lottery game, if six balls are drawn one at a time from a jar containing 49 balls numbered consecutively from 1 to 49, the withdrawal of each ball eliminates it from the next draw, setting up a situation involving *combinations*, described below. However, each *new* drawing of six balls *is* independent from the previous drawing, provided all previously drawn balls are replaced. The mathematics used for calculating the number of combinations of 6, for example, comes under the general heading of *Permutations* and *Combinations*.

PERMUTATIONS An arrangement of a certain number of items is called a *permutation*.

Given that position is important, if one has 5 different objects (A, B, C, D, and E), in how many unique ways can they be placed in groups of 3?

They can be arranged ADE, AED, DEA, DAE, EAD, EDA, ABC, ACB, BCA, BAC and so on. The answer is — in 60 ways.

A good way to visualize permutations is to ask: "In how many different ways can n dinner guests be seated in n chairs?" Starting with one guest and one chair, one way is possible. There are two ways for two guests and two chairs, six ways for three guests and three chairs, and so on. The mathematical expression for counting permutations is $n!$, or "n factorial."

$$n! = 1 \times 2 \times 3 \times 4 \times \ldots \times n$$

Math Behind the Math

Use with Chapter 13.

Have students do an experiment with four chairs and four people, actually counting and recording all the possible arrangements. They should count 24 possible arrangements.

COMBINATIONS An arrangement of a certain number of items in which order is *not* important is called a *combination*.

Given that position is *not* important, if one has 5 different objects (A, B, C, D, and E), in how many ways can they be grouped as 3 objects?

They can be arranged ABC, ABD, ABE, ACD, ACE, ADE, and so on. But CBA is not counted because it has the same letters as ABC. The answer is — in 10 ways.

An everyday example of combinations are the lottery games commonly played within the United States. Nearly every state uses these games to generate state revenue. Students might be surprised by the result, after calculating the total number of possible lottery ticket combinations. The general question is: "How many ways are there to pick n items from a group of N unique items, without replacement?" For the lottery noted above, $N = 49$ balls and $n = 6$ balls. First, there are 49 choices for the first ball, only 48 left for the second, down to 44 for the sixth ball. So, $49 \times 48 \times 47 \times 46 \times 45 \times 44$ is equal to the total number of ways to pick 6 balls. But there is one more thing needed to get the answer. In many lotteries, the *order* in which the balls are picked does not matter. There are $6 \times 5 \times 4 \times 3 \times 2$, or 720, ways to arrange the 6 balls. All 720 of these ways are equivalent, according to the rules of the lottery. So, the product of $49 \times 48 \times 47 \times 46 \times 45 \times 44$ must be *divided* by 720 to get the total number of outcomes. The result is 13,983,803. The probability of winning this lottery on one combination of six numbers is then the microscopic value of $\frac{1}{13,983,803}$.

Lessons 13.4–13.7

DISPLAYING DATA Lesson 13.4 reviews the graphs students have used many times before — bar graphs, circle graphs and line graphs.

These graphs differ in how they are used, and by what type of data they can be used for. Bar graphs and circle graphs are used only with a small set of data, usually no more than 6 or 8 items, although the business section of newspapers often show bar graphs with hundreds of data items. The stock market averages for every weekday of the last year is presented in a bar graph. Both bar graphs and circle graphs also separate the data into categories, unlike many other types of graphs. Line graphs can be used with sets of data from 5 or 6 items to hundreds of items. The data in line graphs are usually sorted chronologically, since most line graphs show changes over time.

Stem-and-leaf plots (introduced in Lesson 13.5) are suited to data sets of moderate size, usually sets of at least 10 items and to nearly 100 items, if the range of the data is large enough. Stem-and-leaf plots separate the data into intervals, instead of categories, and unlike the graphs of lesson 13.4, individual pieces of data do not get lost. When you complete the plot, you can still locate every piece of data. Stem-and-leaf plots ease the burden of ordering large sets of data and are easy for students to create, especially if they use graph paper.

Box-and-whisker plots (introduced in Lesson 13.6) can be used for data sets with anywhere from about 10 items to thousands of items. It is more abstract than other types of graphs students have used before, because all pieces of individual data are lost. The only thing that remains is a sense of the spread and variability of the data. Students will see this type of graph often in the educational careers, because the results of the standardized are often reported in box-and-whisker plots, using an icon to locate their score in relation to the scores of all the other test takers.

Lesson 13.7 focuses on selecting the appropriate graph for a given set of data. The size and organization of a data set usually narrows the choice to one or two types. The purpose for which the data will be used will determine the final selection.

Chapter 13: Tips for New Teachers

Use with Chapter 13.

Lesson 13.1

INCLUSION Some students, especially those acquiring English, may confuse the terms *outcomes* and *events*. To help students see how the two terms are related, use Example 2a. List the outcomes for the experiment. Then identify the event for the experiment from the outcomes in the lists. For example, for Example 2a, show the following display.

Possible Outcomes

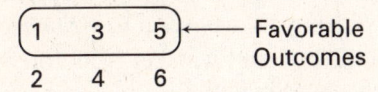

(1   3   5) ← Favorable Outcomes
  2   4   6

INCLUSION For students unfamiliar with the word *complement*, explain that it is related to the word *complete*. Two *complementary events* include the *complete list* of outcomes of an experiment. You may also want students to notice that the sum of the probabilities of two complementary events is 1.

Lesson 13.2

TEACHING TIP For Example 2, be sure students understand the organization of the table. The first three rows show all the combinations that contain nuts, the next two rows show the remaining combinations that contain sprinkles, and the last row shows the one combination that contains caramel that has not been already listed. Have students note that the first topping can be combined with three others, but that the next topping can only be combined with two others because the combination of sprinkles and nuts was already listed.

COMMON ERROR Some students may confuse *combinations* and *permutations*. This is easy to do because combinations in real life often include lists in which order is important. Emphasize that to permute a set of objects is to change their order. So, permutations are lists in which order matters. In lists of combinations, order *does not* matter.

Lesson 13.3

INCLUSION To help students understand the meaning of *independent events*, have them tell you what an independent nation is. Independent nations are ones that are not controlled by another governing body. In a similar fashion, independent events are two events that exert neither control nor influence over the other. Tossing a nickel and a dime and recording their outcomes are independent events. Choosing one of the letters *A* through *E*, setting it aside, and choosing another letter from the remaining four letters are dependent events. This is because the probability of choosing a *D* the second time depends on whether or not a *D* was picked the first time.

TEACHING TIP For Example 3, have students note that using a table for this example would not work. Because tables have only room for two lists of outcomes, there would be no way to include the outcomes of the third event in it. Only a tree diagram works when listing three or more events.

Lesson 13.4

TEACHING TIP When drawing bar graphs, a large break in the scale is often more helpful than misleading. A good example of this is reviewing several weeks of the stock market average. This average has a changing value, usually worth several thousands of points. A rise or fall of 100 points is barely noticeable when a full scale is used. This difference of a few hundred points can have a great financial impact on many people. This is why the title "Potentially Misleading Graphs" is used in Example 1. Graphs with broken scales are often used, but unless they are read carefully, they can be misleading.

TEACHING TIP Before teaching Example 2, list the three averages—*mean*, *median*, and *mode*—on the board. Have students tell how each average is found. When teaching Example 2, have students calculate all three averages. Then ask students to decide which one best describes the middle of the data. Students should justify their answers. The mode, $65, is low for a middle value because all the other prices are greater than this one. The median, $97.50, and the mean, $109, both represent a reasonable middle point for the data.

Tips for New Teachers
Use with Chapter 13.

Lesson 13.5

TEACHING TIP Have students create their stem-and-leaf plots on graph paper, writing only one stem or one leaf in a square. This way the relative frequency of each stem is clearly visible. The stem-and-leaf plot then resembles a bar graph, with each set of leaves showing the frequency of its stem.

TEACHING TIP You may want to show students how they can use the ordering of the leaves on the stem-and-leaf plot to find the median. For Example 2, the stem-and-leaf shows 18 leaves, so the median is halfway between the ninth and tenth leaves. Count the leaves from left to right, top row to bottom row, and circle the ninth and tenth leaves. The median is halfway between these two pieces of data, 12 and 12. So, the median age is 12.

COMMON ERROR Some students may forget to include a stem of 0 when it is needed. Remind them that on a stem-and-leaf plot, the number 9 is represented by 09.

Lesson 13.6

TEACHING TIP Suggest that students organize the data sets into stem-and-leaf plots before making a box-and-whiskers plot. Then they can use the ordered set of data in the stem-and-leaf plot to identify the *median* and the *quartiles*.

Use a slash to indicate where the median appears. Draw the slash between the two numbers for a data set with an even number of items. Draw the slash over the data point for a data set with an odd number of items. This way it is easy to see that the median itself is not included in either the upper half or the lower half of the data, a common error. Using the data for Example 1, the stem-and-leaf plot would look like the following:

```
0 | 9
1 | 2 4 8 9
2 | 2 4 5 7
3 | 6
4 | 2
```

TEACHING TIP Some students may be confused by box-and-whisker plots because the two parts of the box and the two whiskers each represents one quarter of the data, and yet they may all be of different lengths, as in Example 1.

Remind students that data does not need to be spread out evenly over its range. Short boxes (and whiskers) mean that this quarter of the data is scrunched close together; long boxes (and whiskers) mean that this quarter of the data is thinly spread. To visualize this idea, you may want to write each piece of data on the box-and-whiskers plot for Example 1, as shown below. If a median or a quartile is not to be included in the half or the quarter of the data, write it below the plot.

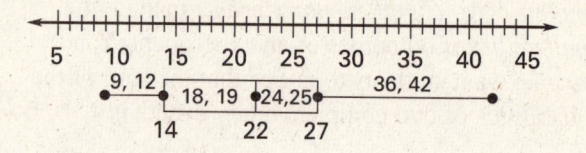

Lesson 13.7

TEACHING TIP Suggest to students that the number of data points in a data set also affects which type of data display they should use. Bar graphs seldom contain more than 8 pieces of data. Line plots become difficult to read after about 25 pieces of data. When the number of data items is greater than 25, it makes more sense to group the data by tens using a stem-and-leaf plot. Box-and-whisker plots need to have at least 8 pieces of data for quartiles to make sense, but they are usually used to display very large sets of data. The size of the data set for circle graphs and line graphs can vary greatly.

CHAPTER 13

Name _____ Date _____

Parents as Partners
Use with Chapter 13.

Chapter Overview One way you can help your student succeed in Chapter 13 is by discussing the lesson goals in the chart below. When a lesson is completed, ask your student the following questions. "What were the goals of the lesson? What new words and formulas did you learn? How can you apply the ideas of the lesson to your life?"

Lesson Title	Lesson Goals	Key Applications
13.1: Introduction to Probability	Write probabilities. Describe complementary events.	• Football Coin Toss • Alphabet • Groundhogs • Raffles
13.2: Finding Outcomes	Use diagrams, tables, and lists to find outcomes. Find combinations and permutations.	• Pottery • Sundae Toppings • Sculptures • Ice Skating
13.3: Probability of Independent Events	Find the probability of two or three independent events.	• Recreation • Carnival • Outfits
13.4: Misleading Statistics	Recognize how statistics can be misleading.	• Movies • Cameras • Storms • Bears
13.5: Stem-and-Leaf Plots	Organize data using stem-and-leaf plots. Find the mean, median, and mode.	• Internet • Diners • Cell Phones
13.6: Box-and-Whisker Plots	Represent data using box-and-whisker plots.	• Ticket Prices • Jellyfish • Solar Eclipses • Bobsleds
13.7: Choosing an Appropriate Data Display	Choose appropriate data displays.	• Stamps • Sunglasses • Weather • Bicycle Stunts

Know How to Take Notes

Summarizing Material is the strategy featured in Chapter 13 (see page 628). This is an excellent tool to help prepare for end of year exams. By taking the effort to summarize the key ideas and relationships, your student is taking strides toward integrating and internalizing the concepts. This will provide a framework within your student's mind for remembering the material much more readily in the future. Learning to organize concepts in this way will make your student a stronger thinker mathematically and will enhance his or her ability to reason.

CHAPTER 13 Continued

Name _____ **Date** _____

Parents as Partners
Use with Chapter 13.

Key Ideas Your student can demonstrate understanding of key concepts by working through the following exercises with you.

Lesson	Exercise
13.1	Your closet contains 7 casual shirts and 3 dress shirts. You randomly choose one shirt. Find the probability that you choose a dress shirt.
13.2	There are two daughters and two sons in a family. Use D (daughter) or S (son) to list all the possible orders of the children from oldest to youngest. Are the orders *combinations* or *permutations*?
13.3	There are four different math classes taught at your school. Students are randomly placed in each math class. What is the probability that both you and your best friend are placed in the same math class?
13.4	A girl sold 7 used bicycles for $100 each and one special racing bike for $800. If the seller wanted to brag that she made a lot on the bikes, what average could she use? What average could she use if she wanted to make the prices seem small?
13.5	Describe and correct the error in the stem-and-leaf plot. Then find the mean, median, and mode of the data. 0 | 3 6 9 10 1 | 1 4 6 2 | 1 7 Key: 2|1 = 21
13.6	Make a box-and-whisker plot for the data in the Lesson 13.5 Question and use it to list the lower and upper quartiles.
13.7	Tell what type of data display you would use for each situation. (a) Show how temperature changed over 8 hours using hourly readings. (b) Show the spread of test scores, including the median and extremes. (c) Show the numbers of students out of 100 that prefer different fruits.

Home Involvement Activity

Directions: Look through various newspapers, magazines or other publications to find different data displays. Try to find a couple of displays that could be misleading. Explain why the display is misleading and how the data should be presented to avoid misinterpretation.

Answers

13.1: $P = \frac{3}{10} = 0.3 = 30\%$ **13.2:** DDSS, DSDS, DSSD, SSDD, SDSD, SDDS; permutations **13.3:** $\frac{1}{4}$ **13.4:** mean: $187.50; mode or median: $100 **13.5:** Leaf 10 in stem 0 should be written as leaf 0 in stem 1; mean: 13; median: 11; mode: none **13.6:** lower: 7.5; upper: 18.5 **13.7:** (a) line graph (b) box-and-whisker plot (c) circle graph

CHAPTER 13

Bulletin Board Idea

Use with Chapter 13.

Objective

To calculate the probability of a sum using two number cubes

Materials

- 1 piece of construction paper
- permanent markers
- sentence strips

Constructing the Bulletin Board

1. On the construction paper, copy the table, which shows the possible outcomes when rolling two number cubes. Label the top row "Roll on Cube 1" and label the first column "Roll on Cube 2." You may want to replace the number at the beginning of each row and each column with a number cube showing the number.

	1	2	3	4	5	6
1	2	3	4	5	6	7
2	3	4	5	6	7	8
3	4	5	6	7	8	9
4	5	6	7	8	9	10
5	6	7	8	9	10	11
6	7	8	9	10	11	12

2. On the first sentence strip, write the title of the table, "Sums When Rolling Two Number Cubes." Place it at the top of the bulletin board.

3. On the second and third sentence strips write the following:
   - How many outcomes are possible when you roll two number cubes?
   - How many different sums are possible? What is the probability of each?

Using the Bulletin Board

After students have completed Lesson 13.3, discuss the bulletin board and its questions with the class. Remind students that the probability of rolling any number on one cube is $\frac{1}{6}$ for each number. However, the probability of rolling a given sum of the two cubes is not the same for all sums. The discussion may include the following.

- Each number cube represents an independent event because the outcome of rolling one cube will not affect the outcome of rolling the other.

- The probability of rolling each sum is equal to the number of combinations that can be rolled to get that sum. For instance, there is only one combination that will produce a sum of 2. The probability of rolling a 2 is $\frac{1}{36}$. However, several combinations will produce the sum of 7, so this sum will have a greater probability.

- Have students create a frequency table by listing the possible sums in the left column and the number of times each sum occurs in the table in the next column.

Follow-up

Using the frequency table, students can add a third column showing the probability of rolling each sum. [2, $\frac{1}{36}$; 3, $\frac{1}{18}$; 4, $\frac{1}{12}$; 5, $\frac{1}{9}$; 6, $\frac{5}{36}$; 7, $\frac{1}{6}$; 8, $\frac{5}{36}$; 9, $\frac{1}{9}$; 10, $\frac{1}{12}$; 11, $\frac{1}{18}$; 12, $\frac{1}{36}$]

Answers

Vocabulary Strategies (pages 15–16)

Lesson 7.2

Simplest Form

What Is It?: A fraction whose numerator and denominator have only the number 1 as a common factor

Comparisons: Unsimplified fraction, such as $\frac{6}{8}$, is not in simplest form.

Improper fraction, such as $\frac{7}{6}$ or $\frac{8}{6}$, may or may not be in simplest form.

Properties: Numerator and denominator cannot be divided evenly by the same whole number (except 1)

May be less than or greater than 1; cannot be equal to 1

May be written as a decimal or a percent

Examples: $\frac{3}{5}, \frac{7}{8}, \frac{11}{8}$

Improper Fraction

What Is It?: A fraction that represents a number greater than or equal to 1

Comparisons: Fraction in simplest form—may or may not be improper

Mixed number—another way of writing an improper fraction

Properties: Value is greater than or equal to 1

Can be written as a whole number or a mixed number, but not both

Can be written as a decimal or percent

Examples: $\frac{3}{2}, \frac{11}{8}, \frac{1250}{100}$

Lesson 13.1

Probability

Definition: A number from 0 to 1 that expresses the likelihood that an event will occur. It is calculated by dividing the number of favorable outcomes by the total number of outcomes.

Facts: Can be written as a fraction, decimal, or percent

Can be either theoretical or experimental

Examples: The probability of tossing heads when tossing a coin is $\frac{1}{2}$, 0.5, or 50%.

The probability of rolling a 6 when rolling a number cube is $\frac{1}{6}$, $0.\overline{16}$, or $16\frac{2}{3}\%$.

Non-examples: The odds of tossing heads on a coin is 1 : 1.

The odds of rolling a 6 on a number cube is 1 : 5.

Odds

Definition: A ratio that compares the number of favorable outcomes to the number of unfavorable outcomes

Facts: Is a part-to-part ratio

Is always written as a ratio, never as a decimal or percent

Examples: The odds of tossing heads on a coin is 1 : 1.

The odds of rolling a 6 on a number cube is 1 : 5.

Non-examples: The probability of tossing heads when tossing a coin is $\frac{1}{2}$, 0.5, or 50%.

The probability of rolling a 6 when rolling a number cube is $\frac{1}{6}$, $0.\overline{16}$, or $16\frac{2}{3}\%$.

Critical Thinking Skills (pages 23–24)

Lesson 5.4

1. In each number the third digit is the sum of the first and the second digit. **2.** All are multiples of 9. **3.** All are multiples of 8.

4. All are cubed numbers. **5.** A snorg is a set of three consecutive two-digit prime numbers. Allow for students who may have a different, but justifiable, definition of a *snorg*.

6. Check students' work.

Lesson 11.7

1. 5:00 **2.** 9:30 **3.** 2:35 **4.** 4:15
5. 11:30 **6.** 1:50 **7.** 8:40
8. 10:20 **9.** 11:20 **10.** Strategies may vary. One effective strategy is to sketch mirror clock faces for each problem.

Strategies for Problem Solving

Strategies for Problem Solving (pages 27–28)

Lesson 1.2
1. 2 **2.** 6; 10 **3.** 170 ft

Lesson 7.7
1. 400 **2.** 19